THE ROYAL LIFE SAVING SOCIETY

FOUNDED 1891. INCORPORATED BY ROYAL CHARTER

Patron:
HER MAJESTY THE QUEEN

Grand President:
ADMIRAL OF THE FLEET
THE EARL MOUNTBATTEN OF BURMA
K.G., P.C., G.C.B., O.M., G.C.S.I., G.C.I.E., G.C.V.O., D.S.O., F.R.S.

UNITED KINGDOM

President:
SIR HENRY STUDDY, C.B.E.

Illustrated Handbook of
Life Saving Instruction

PRICE 4s. 6d. *plus postage*

1st EDITION, 1963
Reprinted 1964
Reprinted 1965
Reprinted 1966
Revised 1967

Published by
THE ROYAL LIFE SAVING SOCIETY
UNITED KINGDOM

Headquarters: Desborough House, 14 Devonshire Str
Portland Place, London, W.1
Telephone: LANgham 5678/5679
Telegrams: Natatorium London

TABLE OF CONTENTS

Page

ii

Note:

All amendments affecting award conditions and details
of life saving methods which have been made in this
revision are sidelined.

ACKNOWLEDGMENTS

THE National Executive has received help and advice in the preparation of this *Handbook* from many and varied sources. It is not possible to acknowledge each separately, but the Committee is conscious of the fact that the members of the General Purposes Committee, the Branch Executive Committees and the Diploma Working Party have devoted much time to the work, and to all those who have been concerned they express their thanks.

The National Executive acknowledges in particular the work of Mr. K. R. Bennetto and Mr. H. P. Hyde, the members of the Handbook Working Party, who devoted very many hours of their time to the collection of material and the writing of the first draft, and the help given by Dr. W. D. W. Brooks, C.B.E., D.M., F.R.C.P. who wrote the section on Physiological and Anatomical considerations.

The National Executive expresses its thanks to the Council of the Royal Life Saving Society—Australia for permission to use certain illustrations and other material contained in the Third Edition of the *Modern Manual of Water Safety and Life Saving*, and to Mr. R. B. Matthews, the Chief Constable of Cornwall, who prepared the notes on surf beaches.

PREFACE

THE Royal Life Saving Society has offered to the general public for more than seventy-five years instruction in methods of saving life from drowning and other forms of asphyxia. During this time more than five million awards have been made by the Society to candidates throughout the Commonwealth who have passed the examinations for its life saving and artificial respiration proficiency awards.

This *Handbook of Instruction* is issued by the National Executive Committee on behalf of the Council of the Royal Life Saving Society—United Kingdom. It is presented to the public as a further contribution to the prevention of loss of life in accidents involving drowning and other forms of asphyxia. Every year such accidents result in the loss of many hundreds of lives, of which a high proportion are the lives of children and young people. The circumstances all too often show that accidents would not have occurred had the need for simple precautions been understood, and that lives have been lost only because of a lack of knowledge of how to act in an emergency.

The Committee expresses the earnest hope that all who pass the Society's examinations will become members of the Society, and that they will forward its purposeful work by forming classes of instruction and encouraging others to learn, so that a knowledge of life saving and artificial respiration may become widespread throughout their country. The Committee also appeals for increased financial support in the form of membership subscriptions, donations and bequests. Without such additional support the work of the Society cannot be expanded.

ADVANTAGES OF MEMBERSHIP

Members of the Society support an organisation which offers a humanitarian service to the general public, and by taking the examinations for the life-saving proficiency awards improve their swimming ability and fitness and their own usefulness as members of the community.

Except as laid down in the general conditions in Part 8 of the *Handbook*, the examinations for the Society's life-saving proficiency awards may only be taken by individual members of the Society, or members of groups (classes, schools, clubs, etc.) affiliated to the Society.

The *Handbook of Instruction* is supplied to individual members and affiliated groups at a reduced price for orders of one dozen or more copies.

Members of the Society receive each year a copy of the Annual Report. They are entitled to wear a tie in the registered colours of the Society, and to purchase and use the Society's car badge.

TERMS OF MEMBERSHIP

A donation of fifteen guineas makes the donor a LIFE GOVERNOR of the Royal Life Saving Society—United Kingdom.

A donation of ten guineas makes the donor a LIFE MEMBER of the Royal Life Saving Society—United Kingdom.

A yearly subscription of a minimum of five shillings constitutes ORDINARY membership of the Royal Life Saving Society—United Kingdom.

Application forms for affiliate membership and details of the fees payable may be had on application to the Headquarters or the appropriate Branch.

PART ONE

INTRODUCTION

1. The aims and objects of the Royal Life Saving Society are

(*a*) To promote technical education in life saving

(*b*) to stimulate public opinion in favour of the

(*c*) to encourage floating, diving, plunging and such

(*d*) to arrange and promote public lectures, demon-

Objects of the Society

2. The foregoing objects were laid down by the
Founders of the Society in 1891, in circumstances very
methods by which help can be given to a person in
methods in that they do not require the use of any

Present day Interpreta-tion of the objects

3. Although the Society is primarily a teaching

annual competitions for the Society's trophies, the foremost of which is the King Edward VII Cup presented to the Society in 1902 by His Majesty King Edward VII who as H.R.H. the Duke of York was the first President of the Society and later became its first Royal Patron, an honour which the Society has since been accorded by each succeeding Sovereign.

Life Guard Corps

4. The Society also encourages the practical application of its teaching by trained life savers through the Life Guard Corps, which provides a service to the community with voluntary patrols at popular bathing places both on the coast and inland. Membership of the Corps is obtained by joining a Life Guard Club and details may be obtained from Headquarters or the Branches.

The Mountbatten Medal

5. The recognition of bravery in the saving of life is the prerogative of the Royal Humane Society, but the Royal Life Saving Society has the privilege of awarding the Mountbatten Medal annually to the holder of one of the Society's proficiency awards who performs the bravest rescue from drowning during the year. The names of winners of the Mountbatten Medal are inscribed on a panel in the Commonwealth Headquarters of the Society, presented by Lord Mountbatten in 1951 and unveiled by Her Royal Highness Princess Elizabeth, Duchess of Edinburgh, who was at that time Vice-Patron of the Society.

History of the Society

6. The history of the Society is summarised in the form of notes at the end of this book.

Supplemental Charter

7. Because of the growth of the Society as a Commonwealth-wide body, the Central Executive, on the advice of the President of the Society, undertook in 1955 a complete review of the organisation set out in the Royal Charter of Incorporation granted in 1924, with particular reference to the management of the

2

Society's affairs in Canada, Australia, New Zealand and South Africa. As a result a Petition was submitted to Her Majesty The Queen who granted a Supplemental Charter to the Society on 27th January, 1960, introducing a new organisation in which the Royal Life Saving Society consisted of five National Societies (the National Branches) in the United Kingdom, Canada, Australia, New Zealand and South Africa, each being self-governing under the general guidance and co-ordination of a Commonwealth Council consisting of the Grand President of the Society, the Deputy Grand President, two representatives of each of the five National Branches, the Honorary Treasurer of the Society and the Chief Secretary.

The National Branches

The Commonwealth Council

8. On 31st May, 1961, South Africa left the Commonwealth and in September of that year the South African Council and Branches of the Society were formed into the South African Life Saving Society which is closely associated with the Royal Life Saving Society.

9. The Royal Life Saving Society—United Kingdom (the United Kingdom National Branch) has responsibility for co-ordinating the work of the Society in all parts of the Commonwealth lying outside the jurisdiction of the other National Branches and consists of:

Organisation of the Royal Life Saving Society— United Kingdom

(a) the Home Branches—the Branches in the United Kingdom and the Leinster, Munster and Connacht Branch.

(b) the Home non-Branch areas—those areas in the United Kingdom, lying outside the Branch areas, in which the work is co-ordinated by Honorary Representatives dealing direct with the Headquarters.

(*c*) the Overseas Branches—the Branches outside the United Kingdom which are represented on the Commonwealth Council by the United Kingdom Members of the Council.

(*d*) the Overseas non-Branch areas—overseas territories in which there are no Branches and in which the work is co-ordinated by Honorary Representatives who deal direct with the Headquarters.

10. The work of the United Kingdom National Branch is guided and co-ordinated by the National Executive, on which each of the Home Branches is represented, under the general supervision of the United Kingdom Council and in accordance with the provisions of a Constitution approved by the Council.

11. The Headquarters of the United Kingdom National Branch are combined for ease of administration and for reasons of economy with the Headquarters of the Commonwealth Society in Desborough House, London.

Lives lost by drowning

12. Every year upwards of a thousand lives are lost by accidental drowning in the sea round the United Kingdom, in the rivers and canals, in enclosed waters such as sand and gravel pits and lakes, in garden ponds, and in homes. Often one-third of the lives so lost are those of young children; others are the lives of brave men and women—and children—who go to the help of people in danger, but because their courage is not matched by an adequate knowledge of how to tackle the job properly, they too lose their lives. The circumstances of some of the fatal accidents, particularly those involving elderly people and very young children, are such that there is often no difficulty in getting the victim out of the water, but life is lost simply because there is no one present who knows how to apply

4

artificial respiration which, if required, must be applied with the absolute minimum of delay, and allows no time to seek the help of others or to look at a book to see how it is done.

13. The drowning problem can be divided under three main headings:

(a) Why do drowning accidents occur?

(b) How can accidents be prevented?

(c) What action must be taken to prevent loss of life if an accident does occur?

THE CAUSES OF DROWNING ACCIDENTS

14. It is not possible to define every circumstance which may lead to a risk of drowning, but the most common causes are:

(a) inadequate supervision of children playing in or near water, and unjustified confidence in the protective value of walls, fences, notices and instruction not to do something, all of which represent a challenge to children and make the forbidden territory all the more attractive;

(b) the use of rubber rings, floats, air beds, etc., without some positive means of restricting their movement into deeper water due to wind, tide, current or other water movement;

(c) the unskilled handling of boats, and the failure to wear personal buoyancy equipment which is essential to the safety of non-swimmers, and often of no less importance to the most competent swimmer who may well be injured or rendered temporarily unconscious by an accident which throws him into the water; sudden immersion in very cold water may also make a swimmer unable to save himself;

(d) the over-confidence of swimmers who swim out at right angles to the shore-line or bank instead of parallel to it; showing off, often with a "dare" behind it;

(e) disregard of warning notices and flags, and underestimation of the dangerous effect of currents, tides, undertows and other circumstances of which they give warning;

(f) diving into, swimming and wading in unknown waters in which there are hidden rocks, tree stumps and other obstructions, mud and weed, steep shelving banks and pot-holes. This applies also to some types of beach in which areas of shallow water are interspersed with deep channels which frequently change their position and direction, and in which the depth of water may increase suddenly due to a change in the gradient;

(g) swimming, fishing and wading alone.

15. The following tables show how the foregoing paragraphs are related to actual fact. They are based on an analysis of drowning accidents in which 622 lives were lost in the United Kingdom in 1965. Table 1 shows the distribution of deaths amongst types of water, and Table 2 the totals attributed to major causes of drowning accidents and the number of children, under three age groups, included in each total.

TABLE 1

Rivers and streams	171	Lakes and reservoirs	43
Sea	129	Sand, gravel and clay	
Canals	62	pits	18
Ponds	53	Swimming baths and	
Homes	46	pools	21
Docks	27	Estuaries	38
		Sewage installations	11

TABLE 2

	Total number of deaths	Number of children involved by age groups		
		0–5	6–10	11–15
Bathing and paddling				
Bathing	35		3	9
Air beds, inner tubes, etc.	4			1
Attempting to rescue another	5			3
Swimming across a river	20		3	9
Retrieving ball, etc.	4	1	2	1
Paddling	7	2	1	1
Fishing	26	4	4	1
Boats	144	1	2	14
Accidents in homes				
Bath	16	3	1	
Ornamental ponds	11	11		
Water-butts, tanks, etc.	10	7		
Home-made rafts	11	2	4	3
Children playing near water outside homes	144	77	55	12
Fall from cliffs	5		1	
Cut off by tide	10			2
Fording streams and rivers	7			2

16. Although they do not lead to drowning accidents, it is thought useful to draw attention here to causes of accidents which result in the loss of many lives each year in homes by other forms of asphyxia

Other causes of asphyxia

for which the immediate first-aid treatment is the application of artificial respiration:

(a) electric shock from defective lighting and heating appliances, electric drills, mowers, hedge clippers, and other tools;

(b) gas poisoning from defective gas fires, cookers and refrigerators;

(c) accidental poisoning.

PREVENTION OF ACCIDENTS

17. Loss of life by drowning is often due to swimmers getting into difficulty when they are out of their depth or too far from land, but neither excessive depth nor distance from dry land is an essential ingredient in a fatal drowning accident. Three to four inches of water are enough to drown a small child who loses his balance and cannot recover. Such quantities of water are inevitable in homes and gardens—in baths and basins, wash-tubs and buckets, gold-fish ponds, water-butts and so on—and they offer an irresistible attraction to an improperly supervised infant. Table 2 on page 7 shows that 21 children in the 0–5 age group died in this way in 1965. In the case of older children the primary hazard lies in rivers, canals, streams and ponds. Natural curiosity, coupled with a lack of any sense of fear, makes them unaware of danger, but once they have fallen into the water it may be only a matter of seconds before they drown if they cannot swim and no help is at hand, even though they may be only a foot or two from the bank. In 1965 the lives of 132 boys and girls under the age of 11 were lost in this way.

Infants

Children

Supervision **18.** Many precautions can be taken to reduce the danger in the case of the smallest children, but proper supervision at all times is the only sure way of preventing an accident. As children become older the

8

effective precautions which can reasonably be taken become fewer. The need is to teach them to swim and to overcome fear of immersion in water so that they will be able to save themselves if they fall in. It is not within the purpose of this book to describe the methods of teaching young children to swim, but it can and should be done from the age of four years; even before that they can be taught the elements of self-confidence in water by demonstration of floating, and so on. Much can be done in the early days of a child's life to teach it to have confidence in and not fear of water, and the need for this early training cannot be overemphasised. Ability to swim

19. The lack of a sufficient number of swimming baths, combined with a climate which restricts out-door swimming to a few weeks in the year, has in the past meant that many children leave school while still unable to swim. Inevitably this situation will continue for some time, but since 1954 a programme for building school swimming baths had been sponsored and developed by the English Schools' Swimming Association, and is resulting in many more children, especially those in the lower age groups, having regular swimming and life saving instruction. Valuable progress has been made possible by schools raising their own funds and by the use of voluntary labour in building the baths. The development of portable pools for elementary swimming instruction has also made a contribution to this problem which is fundamental to the reduction of the toll of lives lost every year by drowning. The ability of every member of the public to swim both for his own safety and for the safety of others is the best possible safeguard for the prevention of drowning accidents. In the words of the Society's Founder, Mr William Henry, printed in the first *Handbook of Instruction*:

"Every citizen should see that the teaching of swimming and life saving *does* form part of our national education."

20. Few drowning accidents occur in swimming baths, and those that do are often attributable to some particular medical condition or other outside cause not normally connected with this type of accident, but many of the fatal accidents which occur elsewhere—all too often during family holidays—can be traced to a false sense of security bred in the victim by the comparative safety of swimming in an enclosed bath, and a lack of understanding of the greater hazards of swimming in open waters. These hazards need not give rise to danger if they are guarded against, but tragedy will often be the result if they are ignored. The following Golden Rules for Bathers, while not exhaustive, should be followed by those who wish to swim and bathe in safety:

A false sense of security

"DOs and DON'Ts" for safety in and on water

DO NOT swim alone, or from lonely, unfrequented and unfamiliar beaches.

DO seek advice from reliable people with local knowledge of sea, river or lake bathing places at a holiday resort.

DO NOT swim out from the beach or bank to a position from which cramp, weeds, obstructions, fatigue, currents, and speed boats or other river craft may endanger your safe return.

DO swim parallel to the shore or bank from which position there will always be a short way home.

DO NOT bathe too soon after a meal, or when hungry.

DO obey implicitly instructions on notice boards giving warning of local dangers. They are put there for your safety.

DO NOT hang your clothes or towel on notice boards giving warning of danger so that others cannot read them.

DO bathe only in the safe areas marked by beach patrol flags or near the centre of a beach.

DO NOT bathe when danger flags are flying or near rocks at the end of a beach.

DO ensure that air mattresses, rings and other types of floats used by children and non-swimmers are restricted in their movement by a line held by a responsible person or secured to some firmly fixed point ashore.

DO NOT take rubber or wooden floats out in waves or surf beyond the point where you can stand upright with a good foothold.

DO be properly trained in the use of underwater swimming apparatus, or use it under super-vision.

DO NOT forget that when you catch up with the beach ball being blown out to sea you have still got to swim back to the beach. It is better to lose a ball than a life.

DO dive through waves when they are about to break on top of you to prevent them over-balancing or submerging you.

DO NOT stay too long in the water, particularly in cold conditions.

DO keep clear of areas near and below diving boards and platforms which are in use.

DO NOT duck others who are less confident in the water than you are.

DO look ahead when surfing or shooting waves to see that you will not collide with other bathers.

DO NOT pretend to be in difficulty when you are not.

DO NOT dive into water the depth of which you do not know, or beneath the surface of which you cannot see. The water may not be deep enough, or there may be rocks, weed, mud or other obstructions which may injure or entangle you.

DO NOT wade or swim out to sea when a ground swell or "sea" is running; a surging mass of water sweeping inshore and then returning seawards can take the strongest swimmer rapidly out of his depth.

DO NOT run, jump or chase others on the sidewalk of a bath, lido or pool; an awkward slip can seriously injure you or others on whom you fall in the water.

DO NOT dive into fast moving water.

If you get into difficulty

(*a*) Keep calm and do not panic;

(*b*) Tread water and rest your arms along the surface of the water. Except when raising them to attract attention do not put them above your head because this will make you sink; alternatively float on your back;

(*c*) Conserve your energy and your breath. If you are being submerged by waves, breathe in deeply when your face is clear of the water;

(*d*) Move slowly and steadily towards quieter water or towards the land. Swim across a current and not against it; this will tire even the strongest swimmer;

(*e*) If the water is choppy, use a side stroke; this will keep the water from your nose and mouth and make breathing easier;

12

(*f*) Keep clear of "breakers" which will sweep you onto the rocks, a pier or groyne.

SURF BEACHES

21. The surf beaches in the United Kingdom are open to the full force of the North Atlantic. Special care has to be taken by those who wish to bathe or use a surf-board. Waves approaching the shore break when the depth of water is too shallow for them to retain their original form. This creates surf. Water brought in towards the beach in this way is removed by a natural drainage system of "rip" currents. These are seaward movements of water confined to different zones. A close study of the sea will generally show their position. On most small surf beaches the surf comes in regularly in the centre and returns by "rip" currents near the rocks at the edges.

REMEMBER that the surf coming in to the beach has got to return to the sea and if you get into one of these "rip" currents you may be carried out. Bathe where the surf is in even lines, generally in the centre of the beach; cross-surf may signify a "rip" current.

REMEMBER not to bathe near rocks.

REMEMBER however good a swimmer you may be in your local swimming bath you are no match for the North Atlantic.

REMEMBER to look for the notices on all popular beaches; these will tell you the particular local dangers.

REMEMBER not to bathe at low water; the sea bed which is not uncovered at some stage of the tide is generally uneven and you may step into a deep channel.

13

REMEMBER to obey the directions of the beachguard. If a safe bathing area is indicated use
this; the beachguard will be able to keep his
eye on you.

REMEMBER not to bathe outside the area; he may
not see you if you get into difficulties.

REMEMBER never to swim alone or in a quiet or
secluded spot where the beach is deserted.

REMEMBER that airbeds should never be taken into
the surf, particularly when the wind is off-
shore; you may be carried far out to sea.

REMEMBER to watch your small children playing
in shallow water; they may easily be knocked
over by a large wave and washed out to sea.

Rescue—Manned Beaches (where Beachguards oper-
ate)

If you get into difficulties raise your arm as a
distress signal. Do not try and battle against the current; wait calmly until help arrives.

Beachguards use a reel and line with a belt attached.
If a rescue takes place and you are asked to man the
line, watch the beltman. He will raise his arm in the
air when he reaches the patient and this is the signal to
pull in. Stand still and, using the hand-over-hand
motion, pull the line in slowly.

*If you pull it in too fast you will pull the rescuer and
his patient under the water and may well drown them
both.*

Rescue—Unmanned Beaches

If you are bathing on a beach where there is no
beachguard you will probably find a reel and line, with

14

belt attached, in a red box. Attached to the notice and platform holding the box you will probably find a hand-operated siren. If someone gets into difficulties, sound the siren by turning the handle; this will summon other people to the beach. If you feel capable of attempting the rescue, carry the box to the water's edge.

Simple instructions for use are on the outside and inside of the lid. Put on the belt. See that those who are going to man the line understand your signal when you reach the patient and tell them to pull in slowly. Swim towards the patient, diving under breaking waves. When you reach him, turn him on his back, grasp him with a firm grip above the elbows. Raise one hand in the air as a signal for those on the beach to commence pulling you in.

If you are pulled in too fast or the line catches in a snag and you wish to release yourself, there is a safety pin fitted to a lanyard in the front of the belt. Pull this upwards and the belt will come apart leaving you free.

When the patient is brought ashore commence artificial respiration at once, if this is necessary.

BOATS

22. The use and handling of boats are not within the scope of this *Handbook*, but every year boating accidents result in loss of life which might have been avoided if two rules had been followed:

(a) Do not leave a capsized boat so long as you can hold on to it safely without being carried over a weir, smashed onto rocks or become injured in some other way;

(b) Have personal buoyancy equipment available and wear it whenever circumstances make that necessary. See that all for whom you are responsible do likewise. The need to wear a life jacket is often closely related to the clothes worn, particularly in cold weather, because they may make it difficult for you to keep afloat if you capsize or fall overboard.

THE PREVENTION OF LOSS OF LIFE

23. The prevention of loss of life if an accident occurs is the first purpose of the Society's teaching, but it cannot be too strongly emphasised that the instruction offered is designed only to instil in the mind of the individual certain basic principles of action, together with methods of release from the drowning clutch (*if it cannot be avoided*) and methods of towing which have been proved by time and experience to be effective. It is not possible to set down in black and white every risk which may have to be considered by a rescuer, or every difficulty which he must overcome. It is only possible to lay down principles supported by examples of the action which can be taken, and the would-be life saver must himself build on these by thought, experiment and practice so that if the need should arise for him to put his knowledge and skill to the test he will automatically act in a way which will give the victim the best chance of survival and reduce the risk to himself to the minimum.

24. The circumstances in which life may be saved from drowning vary widely; on the one hand it may only be necessary to lift a baby out of a bath, or to throw a rope to someone in a river; on the other hand it may be necessary to swim perhaps two hundred yards through a rough sea and bring a panic stricken and struggling victim back to the beach. Swimming ability will often be a controlling factor in the decision whether a would-be rescuer can help or not, and The import- in *any* drowning accident artificial respiration may be the deciding factor between life and death of the victim. It is the duty of *everyone*, old and young, swimmer and

The importance of artificial respiration

16

non-swimmer alike, to know how to apply this essential first-aid treatment should the need arise.

THE AWARDS OF THE SOCIETY

25. It is human nature to try to help someone in danger and it is a simple form of personal insurance to know how to tackle the job properly. The Society offers a series of graded awards indicating proficiency in its life saving teaching—the Elementary Certificate, the Unigrip Certificate, the Intermediate Certificate, the Bronze Medallion, the Bronze Cross, the Award of Merit, the Distinction Award and the Diploma of the Society. In addition there are two Artificial Respiration awards which require no swimming ability. There are also two Safety Awards to show a standard of competence prior to participating in sports on or in the water and as an introduction for younger children to life saving instruction.

26. The Elementary Certificate is an introductory award designed to encourage interest; the Intermediate Certificate indicates limited proficiency in life saving. The standard proficiency award is the Bronze Medallion. The Society considers that holders of this award are fully capable of saving life, but recognises that in an accident only the rescuer who is on the spot can decide whether he is competent to tackle the particular situation, or whether the circumstances are such that an attempt to help would only result in further loss of life. The Society does not claim that the Bronze Medallion qualifies every holder to attempt to save life in every circumstance, but this award indicates at the time of qualification a degree of proficiency adequate to tackle the circumstances in which a high proportion of the drowning accidents occur in the United Kingdom, remembering that many of them are in rivers, canals, sand-pits, etc.

17

27. The Bronze Cross, Award of Merit and Distinction Awards indicate a higher degree of practical life saving proficiency together with greater stamina. The Diploma requires theoretical knowledge in addition to a high standard in practical life saving skills.

Bars to the awards **28.** Holders of the Society's awards are encouraged to keep in practice by periodical requalification which is recognised by the granting of bars to the Bronze Medallion, Bronze Cross and Award of Merit.

The purpose of the Society **29.** In summary the primary purpose of the Royal Life Saving Society is to reduce the loss of life, by bringing home to members of the general public the causes of drowning accidents, by encouraging a widespread ability to swim, and by instilling in the maximum numbers a knowledge of simple methods by which loss of life can often be prevented—knowledge which too often remains unlearnt until personal tragedy brings home the need for it together with the realisation, *too late*, that a life need not have been lost. The value of this work is proved almost daily by the successful use of the Society's methods of rescue somewhere in the Commonwealth.

MAKING A RESCUE

Fear **30.** Fear is the greatest enemy of a person in difficulty in water because it saps his confidence in his ability to help himself, and gives rise to panic. It follows that the first requirement of a rescuer is to calm the victim's fear: when circumstances permit this can be done by talking to the victim and acting with Speed of action calm confidence. At the same time speed of action is essential because the victim may give up hope and sink, he may become unconscious or he may already be in a state of asphyxia, in which case the application of artificial respiration at the earliest possible moment may be the only hope of saving his life.

31. It is not always necessary, or the best action, What to do for a rescuer to enter the water to save someone else. The courses of action open to a rescuer are summarised in the words *Reach—Throw—Wade—Row—Swim—Tow*, and he must first of all sum up the situation and decide which of these courses to adopt.

REACH. The victim may be so close to the bank that a hand stretched out to him is all that is required. Lying down on the bank will not only make it less likely that the rescuer will be pulled into the water, but will also increase his reach. If the victim cannot be reached with a hand, there may be a pole, branch of a tree, or some other object handy which can be held out to him.

THROW. If the victim is out of reach, throw a rope to him if one is handy, but do not go away to look for one; this may be the last straw if he thinks that you are abandoning him. Failing a rope, some object which will float—a log of wood, a beach ball, the seat of a car, etc.—thrown near him will give him support and an immediate return of confidence and you valuable time to think what can best be done next.

WADE. Wading is usually quicker than swimming and you may be able to carry a pole or something else which you can hold out to the victim and then pull him into shallow water.

ROW. If you can row and a boat is immediately available, rowing will be quicker than swimming if the victim is some way out; the sight of an approaching boat will do much to restore his confidence.

SWIM AND TOW. If none of the above actions are possible then the rescuer must swim out to the victim and tow him back to safety.

19

32. There is no hard and fast rule by which the above measures can be applied to any particular set of circumstances. Each emergency must be considered on its merits and the practical life saver will by thought and practise form an ability to sum up a situation, which often requires resourcefulness and judgement, and then act calmly and confidently with the maximum speed.

The need for thought and practice

Entry into the water

33. If it is necessary to swim to him, the condition of the victim and his distance from land will govern the time available to the rescuer and his decision whether or not to remove his outer clothing and shoes. No set rule can be given, but in general a few seconds doing this are well spent unless the distance is very short. A rescuer who is exhausted when he reaches the victim will fail in his purpose which is to get both safely back to land.

34. The method of entry into water from various types of "take-off" requires thought. A dive or a plunge will gain distance and perhaps valuable seconds, but a rescuer who hits his head on a submerged rock, cuts an artery on the jagged end of a broken bottle or becomes entangled in weeds will not achieve his purpose or be of any help to the victim. He will simply become an additional liability. If the depth of water and nature of the bottom are not known, entry should **always be feet-first.**

35. The line of sight to the victim may not always be the quickest path to reach him. For example, in a fast-flowing river it may sometimes be of advantage to run along the bank to a position from which you can swim across the stream to cut-off the victim as he is carried down by it. On a beach there may be a sand spit near-by along which you can run or wade and so shorten the distance to be covered by swimming.

36. To all but the most experienced practical life saver the swim out to the victim is the most difficult factor in a rescue to judge correctly. Speed is essential, but it is equally essential that the rescuer should arrive with sufficient energy remaining to take the victim in tow and bring him to safety—and perhaps then to apply artificial respiration if no other help is available. This requires judgement, determination and stamina when the distance is more than a few yards. In the sea the return journey will probably have to be made over much the same distance as the outward swim, but in a river, canal or lake there may be land nearer than the point of departure, particularly if use is made of the direction of flow of the water.

37. Fear gives abnormal strength to a person in danger of drowning and he will clutch fiercely and relentlessly at anything coming within his reach. Some years ago a fully grown man, attempting to rescue a 7-year-old boy, allowed the boy to get a grip round his throat which he was unable to release. He became unconscious in less than one minute and had himself to be rescued. Although the Society's teaching includes methods of releasing a drowning clutch, it can not be too strongly emphasised that the first purpose of the rescuer when approaching the victim must be to *avoid* being clutched. One way is to "stand off" from the victim and to restore his confidence by explaining that you are there to help him and require his co-operation by doing what you tell him to do. You may even be justified in telling him that you will leave him if he doesn't co-operate. If this fails, attempt to get behind him, moving round out of his reach, or by diving and approaching him under the water. If the rescuer is clutched, the appropriate method of release must be applied with absolute determination; this is a life and death struggle in which half measures are not only useless, but may also be dangerous to the rescuer.

21

38. The method of tow will depend on the rescuer's preference, the state of the water and the state of the patient, who may be conscious and co-operative, un-co-operative and struggling or unconscious. Recommended methods of towing are described elsewhere in this book, but they are by no means exhaustive; a rescuer may find some quite unorthodox method best suited to the circumstances, or he may need to change from one to another during the return swim.

39. Methods of landing the patient are described in Part 5 of the book. The circumstances may vary from just giving a helping hand to an exhausted but conscious person over a shallow shelving beach, to hoisting an unconscious body up a steep river bank without other help. This is an essential part of the rescue in which speed may be of vital importance if artificial respiration is required. If the proper methods are learnt a seemingly impossible task can often be done with speed and comparative ease, even when the patient is larger and heavier than the rescuer.

40. Methods of artificial respiration and the characteristic signs demonstrating a need for its application are described in Part 7. If it is required, every second of delay before starting counts. Once the victim of an accident has ceased to breathe it is only a matter of minutes before he is beyond help, the interval being shorter in fresh-water drowning than in salt-water drowning. Nevertheless the ordinary layman is not competent to assess the true state of a patient who may appear dead but may not be so, and artificial respiration should *always* be applied, no matter how useless it may appear; it should be continued without ceasing until a doctor has declared the patient dead or until signs of rigor mortis are apparent. The Expired Air method can be used to give a few vital breaths immediately the rescuer gets his feet on the ground, and

22

a strong swimmer can attempt this even before reaching shallow water. The method used subsequently will be a matter of circumstance or choice by the rescuer, but the Expired Air method (mouth-to-nose) undoubtedly has the best chance of success.

41. Only when the patient's breathing has been restored can the rescuer divert his attention to summoning help. Even then the patient must be watched to ensure that his breathing does not again cease, and he must be given such care as is possible to reduce the effect of shock. Every victim of a drowning accident should be kept under medical supervision until discharged by a doctor. (See paragraph 600.)

LEARN TO HELP OTHERS

42. The foregoing paragraphs outline the sequence of events in a drowning accident, and underline the causes of such accidents and the steps which can be taken to prevent them. The remaining parts of this book amplify those paragraphs and offer instruction in methods which have been proved effective by many years of experience. They are commended to all who wish to equip themselves to help others in a drowning emergency, and particularly to all who obtain pleasure and enjoyment from swimming, because they have a moral responsibility to know how to swim not only for their own safety, but also for the safety of others.

PART TWO

SWIMMING STROKES AND MOVE-MENTS USED IN LIFE SAVING

200. Speed is essential in life saving because the victim of an accident may sink before the rescuer can reach him, or he may already be in a state of asphyxia and in urgent need of artificial respiration, but when deciding which stroke(s) to use the rescuer must balance the need for speed against the distance which he has to cover, and the water conditions, waves, wind, current and so on. He must conserve sufficient energy to bring both his patient and himself to safety, otherwise his efforts will be useless. It is not a purpose of this *Handbook* to describe swimming strokes generally because it is assumed that candidates for the Society's proficiency awards will already be reasonably competent swimmers before commencing their life saving training, but the following notes are included because the strokes and movements described have a particular application to life saving.

LIFE-SAVING BACK-STROKE

201. The double-action back-stroke leg kick is shortened so that emphasis is on that part of the leg below the knee. Keeping the upper part of the legs in line with the body, the feet are lowered gently from the knees, as the knees open sideways, until they are directly below the former position of the knees. The movement is a short continuous circular action from the knees, the insteps and the shins pressing against the resistance of the water. The driving force is principally produced by the front of the lower part of the legs and the front and insides of the feet. The extended legs come together in line with the body. The advantage of this stroke is that the continuous movements produce steady progress, without jerking, through the water, but it is a tiring method if the tow has to be made over more than a short distance. Over a longer distance the speed advantage will probably lie with the method in which a stroke and rest are alternated.

SIDE-STROKE

202. The advantage of the side-stroke is that it is simple to perform and requires a relatively small energy output, although the leg action provides good propulsive power. It can give protection to the face in choppy water, forward vision is satisfactory and breathing is unrestricted. The arms can be changed periodically. The body is straight and laid on one side, Start and glide position with the side of the face resting in the water. Assuming the swimmer to be on his right side, the right arm is extended fully forward beyond the head with the palm of the hand downwards. The left arm is along the left side of the body. During the glide the right Arm action arm begins its stroke pulling with a shallow sweep through the water back to the shoulder; the elbow is bent and the wrist is extended to continue the sweep backwards as a circular movement. If not being used in towing a subject, the left arm glides forward, palm downwards, to a position just forward of and below the face, the elbow being kept close to the body and well bent. It then makes a backward pull just below the surface and finishes alongside the thigh. The movements of the two arms are co-ordinated, the backward movement of the left arm coinciding with the forward movement of the right arm. If the swimmer is on his left side the above arm movements are reversed. The legs recover by bending at the knees Leg action and hips while the right arm is completing its backward movement. They are then extended, both legs moving parallel to the surface of the water, to close

2

with a flip of the ankles and feet. The leg thrust is obtained by extending the legs and ankles, and scissoring them towards each other. At the same time the left arm recovers its forward position. If the upper leg (in this case the left leg) is forward the swimmer is using the orthodox scissor kick; if the lower leg is forward he is using the inverted scissor kick.

SURFACE DIVE

203. A surface dive is used to descend from a swimming position to recover a body or other object below the surface. The descent can be either head-first or feet-first. The head-first method gives full vision during the descent, and the hands are ready to grasp, ward off obstructions and give impetus by pulling. A feet-first descent is useful when the depth is not great and when searching a muddy area.

Head-first   204. The rescuer swims breast-stroke or crawl-stroke to a position 6 feet from a point immediately above the body or object. The arms are thrust deep into the water and the hands turned to make a breast-stroke, the pull being upwards towards the surface of the water. At the same time the head and shoulders are turned sharply down into the water, the hips raised, and the legs are lifted clear of the water. In the final stage the arms and the body are straightened into line for the downward plunge. The purpose of raising the legs clear of the water and vertically above the hips is to use their weight to drive the body down through the water. Added depth can be gained by swimming down, using a breast-stroke pull, sweeping the arms to the sides, and the legs using a breast-stroke or crawl kick.

Feet-first   205. The dive is made immediately over the point of search. With the body in an upright position and as low as possible in the water, give a strong breast-stroke

26

kick with the legs and at the same time press downwards with the hands from the surface of the water so as to raise the body as high as possible out of the water. Take a deep breath, raise the arms vertically above the head and point the toes with the legs together. As the face submerges allow a little air to escape from the nose to prevent the entry of water. As soon as the hands are submerged they should be used in an upward sculling motion above the head to keep the body down. A walking or circular motion of the legs is used to feel for the object on the bottom.

SEARCH FOR A BODY

206. For reasons of safety, and because the majority of examinations in the United Kingdom are carried out in clear water in swimming baths, a search for an object is not included in the examinations for the Society's awards. In an actual accident the victim may sink below the surface, but not necessarily to the bottom, before the rescuer can reach him. In this case prompt and decisive action will reduce the area of search because the victim may be carried away by tide or current from the point at which he was last seen. In good light and clear water the rescuer may be able to see the body by remaining on the surface of the water with his face submerged. In bad light or cloudy water a search may be necessary at more than one depth. Bubbles of air rising to the surface may show the position of the body, but they are not easily seen by a rescuer who is himself in the water. If there is a tide or current allowance must be made for the fact that the bubbles will not rise vertically but will be carried away in the direction of flow of the water from the position of the body during their passage to the surface, the distance being dependent on the depth at which the body is. Without special training the average person cannot remain under water for more than 30

27

seconds without risk of becoming unconscious. In some cases this period may be even shorter. For this reason a succession of short quick dives is better than a prolonged search which may render the rescuer incapable of helping either the victim of the accident or himself.

FEET-FIRST ENTRY INTO THE WATER

207. When an entry by dive or jump into the water must be made, a feet-first entry should be used when the depth of water and nature of the bottom are not known. When there are no known hazards the jump should be used to make as much distance towards the victim as possible. The legs can be opened or closed in flight. Leg-open flight will check a deep entry, but it should be used only from low heights. The legs should be kept together when jumping from a height of 8 feet or more, a deep entry being prevented by opening the legs immediately they are in the water, but not before, and giving a strong breast-stroke kick, at the same time spreading the arms wide. A fast cycling action with the legs will also help to prevent a deep entry. During flight the body should be inclined slightly forward, the head in line with the body and the chin tucked in. A position in flight which is too far backward can give a painful entry. If the position is over-balanced forward the knees should be bent up to take the impact with the water. The nose should be held between the thumb and index finger to prevent the entry of water. The body must be controlled, being neither too rigid nor too relaxed; either can cause injury.

SCULLING

208. The swimmer turns onto his back, keeping his body horizontal, legs together, and toes pointed and showing just above the surface. The arms are kept straight and close to the sides of the body, with the wrists loose. Propulsion through the water is obtained Head-first by a sculling action of the hands at the hips. The fingers and thumbs are kept closed, and slightly bent to form a cup, and the hands are "flapped" outwards in a continuous circular movement to push the water towards the feet. By reversing the movement and push- Feet-first ing the water towards the head the body will be propelled feet-first. Stretch the feet well and look towards them without lifting the back of the head out of the water; this will avoid hollowing the back which causes the legs to sink.

UNDERWATER APPROACH

209. At a point well away from the victim, the rescuer executes a surface dive to a position in front of and **below** the victim's feet. He then swims diagonally upwards and grasps the patient immediately above the knees and in one motion turns the patient around smartly. The rescuer then slides his hands up the patient's sides until he is about to surface, when one hand is placed in a towing position.

Unless visibility below the surface is satisfactory the rescuer should not use this method because:

    (i) He may lose sight of the victim.

   (ii) He may be kicked by the victim.

  (iii) He may be clutched if he surfaces near the victim.

RELEASE FROM A DROWNING CLUTCH

300. It has been explained in paragraph 37 that when approaching a person in danger of drowning the first purpose of the rescuer must be to avoid being clutched. Nevertheless all attempts to do this may sometimes fail, and a life-saver must know how to release himself if necessary. There are many ways in which a person may clutch his rescuer, and it is only possible in a *Handbook of Instruction* to give examples, together with proved methods by which such clutches can be broken. By learning these basic methods candidates for the Society's proficiency awards will gain a knowledge of the general principles to be applied to any grip, but the certainty of using the right action on any particular occasion will come only from continued thought and practice. The rescuer's action must be sudden and vigorous to make the drowning person release his grip, if necessary as the result of physical pain or from fear of being submerged. As explained in paragraph 37, in an actual rescue a quick release from a drowning clutch may be a matter of life or death to the rescuer and he must be prepared to use the degree of force necessary to achieve his overall purpose of bringing the victim of an accident, and himself, safely to land.

301. Candidates for the Intermediate Certificate and the Bronze Medallion will be required to know how to perform one method of release from each of the following types of clutch—wrist, neck, body and a clutch from behind. Candidates for higher awards may be required to demonstrate any of the following methods.

WRIST GRIP

Double wrist twist break

302. The subject grips the wrists or lower arms of the rescuer. To release the grip the rescuer brings his arms downwards and outwards in a circular movement, the whole action being one vigorous and continuous movement. If the subject retains his grip this movement will turn his hands inwards as the rescuer

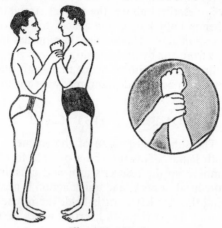

Illustration No. 1.

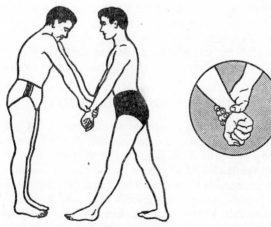

Illustration No. 2.

31

brings his arms down, and will put backward pressure on his thumbs causing him to release his grip as the rescuer swings his arms outwards.

303. As an alternative to the method of releasing a wrist grip described above, the rescuer straightens his arms, bends both knees, and places his feet on the subject's shoulders. The rescuer than pushes the subject away from him by straightening his legs vigorously. By pushing harder with one foot than with the other the subject can be turned round ready for towing.

DOUBLE WRIST GRIP

304. The subject grips one of the rescuer's wrists with both hands. This may be a prelude to the subject climbing up the rescuer's arm and grasping him round the head or neck, and quick action is necessary. Assuming that his left wrist is held, the rescuer grips the subject's right wrist with his right hand, his thumb being on the outer side, and bears down on the subject's arm. At the same time the rescuer swings his right leg up over the subject's left arm and places his foot on the subject's left shoulder. By holding the subject's wrist firmly and pushing vigorously on his shoulder by straightening the leg the grip will be broken and the subject can be turned ready for towing.

GRIP ROUND THE BODY

305. The subject grasps the rescuer round the body enclosing his arms. To release the grip the rescuer bends one arm up and grips the subject's shoulder from the back. At the same time he brings his other arm up, outside the subject's arm, and places the palm of his hand under the subject's chin, and breaks the grip by forcing the subject's chin upwards and backwards, retaining the grip on the subject's shoulder.

Illustration No. 3.

306. As an alternative to the above method the rescuer grasps the subject with his hands placed between the subject's waist and armpits. He then takes a deep breath, forces his elbows outwards and upwards and slides out of the grip by submerging with his chin tucked well into his shoulder. While submerged he turns the subject to a towing position.

Lift and slide break

Illustration No. 4.

GRIP ROUND THE NECK AND FRONT STRANGLEHOLD

Back and chin break

307. The subject locks his hands at the back of the rescuer's neck. To release the grip the rescuer places one hand in the small of the subject's back and brings his other hand up outside the subject's arm, places the heel of his hand under the subject's chin and grips the subject's nose between his outstretched fingers. The rescuer then pulls the subject towards him with the hand in the small of his back, and, at the same time, pushes the subject's chin upwards and backwards until he releases his grip.

Illustration No. 5.

308. Alternative methods of releasing a front stranglehold are:

Elbow jerk break

(*a*) The rescuer places his hands under the elbows of

34

the subject. He then takes a deep breath, jerks the subject's elbows up sharply and submerges with his chin tucked well in. While submerged the rescuer grasps the subject by the waist and turns him to the towing position.

(b) The rescuer places the palm of his right hand under the subject's left elbow and his left hand behind the subject's right shoulder. He then pushes the subject's elbow upwards and backwards, at the same time ducking his head away from the subject. As the grip is released the subject is turned to the towing position by pulling on his shoulder.

Elbow and shoulder turn break

(c) The following method can be used if the subject's head is over the rescuer's shoulder. Assume that the subject's head is over the rescuer's right shoulder. The rescuer brings his right hand up outside the subject's left arm and places his hand against the subject's right cheek with the thumb hooked under his jaw. At the same time the rescuer grips the subject's right arm at the elbow with his left hand. By forcing the subject's head outwards and round with the right hand, and pushing his elbow up with the left hand, the grip will be broken and the rescuer can duck his head out of it and turn the patient to a towing position.

Elbow and cheek twist break

(d) The subject grips the rescuer from the front with his hands tightly round the rescuer's throat. The rescuer grasps the subject's arms firmly at his elbows, and presses sharply upwards and inwards, forcing the subject to release his grip by reverse pressure on his elbow joints. After release the rescuer retains his grasp to turn the subject to a towing position.

Elbow pressure break

BACK STRANGLEHOLD

Chin drop and submerge break

309. If the rescuer is clutched from behind with his upper arms pinioned he should immediately protect his throat by dropping his chin into his chest. He then grasps the arms of the subject, takes a deep breath and, bending forward from the waist, submerges. If this fails to dislodge the subject one of the following methods must be used:

Wrist and elbow break

(a) The rescuer grips one of the subject's wrists with his opposite hand (left wrist—right hand or vice versa) and the subject's same arm at the elbow with his free hand. He then pushes the subject's elbow up and at the same time forces the lower arm downwards and inwards with his other hand. Turning his head away from the gripped elbow, the rescuer ducks under the subject's arm, releases his grip on the elbow and carries the subject's arm round behind the subject's back, keeping it there until the subject is in the towing position.

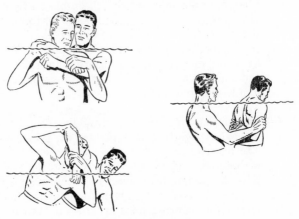

Illustration No. 6.

36

(*b*) Grip the subject's thumbs—or one thumb and the opposite wrist—and force them apart by pressure against the joints. Spread his arms wide and get clear.

Thumb or thumb and wrist break

(*c*) Take a deep breath, bend forward from the waist and somersault forwards.

Somersault break

REAR WAIST HOLD

310. The subject grasps the rescuer round the waist leaving his arms free. The rescuer grips the subject's thumbs and forces his hands apart by pressure against the joints. Alternatively, the rescuer reaches backwards over his head, grasps the subject by his hair or head. He then takes a deep breath, bends forward and pulls the subject over his head.

Thumb pressure break

Pull over head break

SEPARATION OF TWO SWIMMERS LOCKED TOGETHER

311. A weak swimmer, or one not trained in life saving, may be clutched and unable to free himself. Similarly two people, finding themselves in difficulty in deep water, may become locked together in a struggle to save themselves. To separate them the rescuer approaches one, the weaker swimmer if known, from behind, grips his chin with both hands and bears down on him with his forearms, submerging both subjects. Keeping his weight over the subject being held by the chin, the rescuer brings one foot over the locked arms of the subjects and places his foot on the chest of the subject not being held. He then straightens his leg to push the two subjects apart, at the same time pulling the subject held by the chin up and back. Care must be taken to ensure that the grip on the subject's chin does not slip down to his throat.

TOWING METHODS

400. The best method of towing a person through the water will depend on whether he is conscious, unconscious, or helpless for some other reason, whether he is co-operative or struggling and resisting help, the state of the water—whether it is rough or calm, the direction and strength of the wind, tide or current, and so on. No set rule can be laid down, and the decision which method of towing to use must rest with the rescuer in each particular case. If the length of the tow is long he may well decide to change from one method to another.

401. Whatever method is used, the grip on the subject must be firm, not only to give him support and to control him if he struggles, but also to give him confidence in the rescuer's ability to help him. A slack grip not only deprives the rescuer and subject of the foregoing advantages, but also results in jerky progress through the water and makes the rescuer's task unnecessarily laborious. A slack grip may also allow the subject to slip from the rescuer's grasp and sink if he should suddenly become unconscious.

402. In the single-handed methods of towing described in the following paragraphs, the right or left hand or arm is referred to for simplicity, but it will be evident that in most cases the arm used to grip the subject is a matter of choice by the rescuer.

UNIGRIP HEAD CARRY METHOD

403. The rescuer places himself behind the subject and passes his left arm over the subject's left shoulder cupping the subject's chin in his left hand. The subject's head rests on the rescuer's left shoulder, and the rescuer secures a firm grip by pressing his bent left arm into the subject's shoulder. The rescuer uses a back-stroke. If the subject struggles he is restrained by the rescuer passing his right arm under the subject's right arm and taking a firm grip on the subject's right shoulder from the front. If further restraint is required, the rescuer grips the subject's nose with the

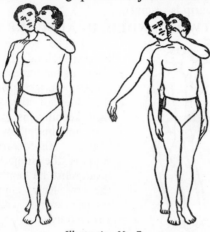

Illustration No. 7.

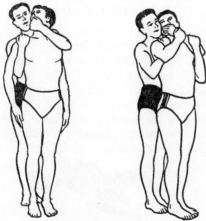

Illustration No. 8.

39

thumb and fingers of his left hand and places the palm of his hand over the subject's mouth restricting his air supply. He will then instinctively pull your hand and arm down onto his chest and hold it there. When the subject has quietened down the original single-handed grip is resumed.

TWO-HANDED HEAD CARRY

404. The rescuer places himself behind the subject and puts his hands, with his fingers pointing upwards, on the sides of the subject's face, keeping his own arms bent and his elbows pulled well in. His forearms then support the subject whose head must be kept close to the rescuer's chin. The rescuer swims with a leg stroke only.

Illustration No. 9.

THE HIP CARRY

405. From behind the rescuer passes his right arm over the subject's right shoulder and grips him in his left armpit, the rescuer's elbow being clamped firmly down on the subject's chest. The rescuer, using the side-stroke, keeps his right hip close up to the small of the subject's back. If the subject struggles, the grip can be tightened by the rescuer placing his left hand under the subject's left armpit clamping his shoulder firmly against the rescuer's chest.

Illustration No. 10.

TWO-HANDED CHEST CARRY

406. From behind the rescuer passes his arms under the subject's arms and places his hands high on the subject's chest with his thumbs resting on the subject's collar bone. The rescuer raises his elbows to support the subject's upper arms at right angles to his body. The subject's head rests on the rescuer's shoulder. The rescuer swims with a leg-stroke only.

TIRED-SWIMMER CARRY

407. The rescuer faces the subject and instructs him to place his hands on the rescuer's shoulders, close to his neck, keeping his arms straight, and to lie back in the water. The rescuer swims, using the breast-stroke, and propels the subject backwards through the water. The subject's legs trail under the rescuer's body and he may be instructed to spread them so as not to impede the rescuer's leg action. If it is necessary to change direction to the left, the rescuer carries his left arm under the subject's right arm and takes a light hold of the subject's left forearm, continuing the swimming stroke strongly with his right arm. The subject can assist the turn by bending his head to his right. When the necessary turn has been made, the breast-stroke is resumed with both arms. To turn to the right the foregoing motions are followed, but substituting "right" for "left", and vice versa.

Illustration No. 11.

SINGLE-HANDED HAIR, CHIN OR CLOTHES CARRY

408. This is an effective method of towing which can be maintained over a long distance. The rescuer takes

41

a firm grip of the hair on the top of the subject's head and swims side-stroke towing the subject at arm's length. In the chin carry the rescuer's hand is cupped under the subject's chin. In the clothes carry a firm grip is taken on the clothing at the back of the subject's neck taking care to ensure that his clothing is sufficiently loose at his throat to prevent restriction of his breathing. If the subject is conscious and co-operative, he can assist the rescuer by stretching his arms above his head and taking a light grip with both hands on the rescuer's wrist or forearm. This will make the tow more rigid. When the hair or chin carry is used, the rescuer must ensure that the subject's nose and mouth are kept clear of the water by flexing his arm or wrist as necessary.

HAIR-CARRY   CHIN-CARRY

CLOTHING-CARRY
Illustration No. 12.

TWO-HANDED ARM CARRY

409. From behind the subject the rescuer takes a firm grip of the subject's arms close above his elbows, the rescuer's fingers being inside and thumbs outside. The rescuer raises the subject's arms to shoulder level allowing his forearms to droop, and tucks his own elbows firmly into his sides to obtain a rigid tow and to prevent the subject struggling or turning. The rescuer swims with a shortened double leg action backstroke.

DOUBLE SHOULDER HOOK

410. From behind, the rescuer passes his arms under the subject's armpits and hooks his fingers over the subject's shoulders. The rescuer's arms are bent at a tight angle, and his elbows are tucked well into his sides to hold the subject firmly on his chest. The rescuer swims with a shortened double leg action backstroke.

DOUBLE CARRY

411. In favourable conditions it is possible for an expert life-saver to tow two subjects simultaneously, by the hair carry, clothes carry or chin carry provided they are co-operative or completely helpless. The rescuer should keep well clear until he is satisfied that the subjects will co-operate and while he explains to them what he intends to do. He then grasps one subject in each hand and swims on his back using an appropriate leg action.

Illustration No. 13.

PART FIVE

LANDING AND CARRYING A RESCUED PERSON

500. A person who has been rescued may, if he is unconscious or unable to help himself for some other reason, have to be lifted from the water and carried to a place of safety or to a place where artificial respiration can be applied. Help may not always be available, and much valuable time can be lost if the rescuer does not know the methods to be used.

501. The following methods are used to lift a patient up a low vertical bank, onto a raft or onto the side of a swimming pool:

CROSSED ARM METHOD

502. Keeping a firm grip on the patient, the rescuer turns himself and the patient to face the bank. The patient's hands are then placed on top of the bank, one hand on top of the other, his arms being stretched up sufficiently to keep his face clear of the water. The rescuer places one of his hands on those of the patient to hold them in position, and climbs onto the bank. Standing, and facing the patient, the rescuer grasps the patient's right wrist in his own right hand, and his left wrist in his own left hand crossing his own arms, but not the patient's to do this. Taking care that the patient's legs are not under the bank, and without submerging his face, the rescuer makes one or two preliminary dips of the patient to gain momentum and then lifts him clear of the water. As the lift is made the rescuer uncrosses his arms and turns the patient bringing him to a sitting position on the bank facing the water. While himself getting out of the water and getting into position to make the lift, the rescuer must maintain his hold on the patient's hands; if this hold is released the patient is likely to slip back into the water and much time will be wasted.

STRAIGHT ARM METHOD

503. In the Straight Arm method the preparatory movements are the same as those for the Crossed Arm method. When on the bank the rescuer faces the patient and, with his knees bent, grasps the patient's left wrist with his own right hand, and his right wrist in his own left hand. The rescuer then straightens his legs and lifts the patient up and over the edge of the bank so that his chest rests on the bank. Then placing one hand firmly on the patient's back to hold him in position, the rescuer uses his other hand to swing the patient's legs up and over the bank.

STIRRUP METHOD

504. The Stirrup method can be used in shallow water when the patient is able to give some co-operation. The rescuer supports the patient against the bank with one hand and, bending down, cups his free hand for the patient to put his foot or knee in it. The rescuer then gives the patient a helping lift up the bank. If the patient does not need support and both the rescuer's hands can be used to form the stirrup, the rescuer can give the patient considerable lift.

FIREMAN'S LIFT

505. In most cases, the easiest way of landing the patient in shallow water is by floating him on the surface and towing him but if it is necessary to *carry* the patient from the water without other help, the Fireman's lift is one method which can be used. When the water is level with the rescuer's hips he floats the patient, face upwards, between himself and the shore. The patient's head may be to the right or left of the rescuer. In the following description the patient's head is assumed to be to the right. In the reverse position the words right and left should be transposed in the description.

506. Facing the patient, the rescuer grasps the patient's left wrist with his right hand and passes his left hand between the patient's legs and round his left thigh. The rescuer then ducks his head under the patient's waist, rolls him over to a face-downwards position on the rescuer's shoulders; the rescuer then stands erect lifting the patient clear of the water. This movement must be made quickly as the patient's face will be momentarily under water. The rescuer then transfers the patient's left wrist to his own left hand, leaving his (the rescuer's) right hand free for use.

Illustration No. 14.

507. If the Fireman's lift is attempted in water which is too deep the patient's face will remain under water. Practise will show the appropriate depth of water. If the method is practised on dry land, the rescuer can suffer injury or strain if it is not done properly.

508. To lower the patient at the end of the carry, the rescuer, if on a slope, faces up the slope and bends at the knees and hips to allow the patient's feet to rest on the ground. Still supporting the weight of the patient on his shoulders the rescuer passes the patient's left arm over his head and then grasps the patient round the chest, supporting the patient's weight on his own arms and chest. The rescuer then takes a short pace

backwards with one foot and lowers the patient onto
his knees, the rescuer taking the patient's weight on his
own forward knee which is slightly bent. At the same
time the rescuer moves his hands upwards to grasp the
patient under his armpits and moves backwards and
down onto one knee to lower the patient into a lying
position on the ground.

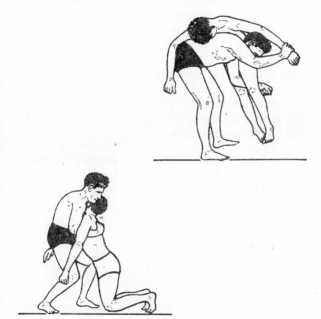

Illustrations No. 15.

SADDLEBACK LIFT

509. The Saddleback method of carrying a patient
makes less demand on the strength of the rescuer, but
it does not leave one of his arms free to help himself if
necessary.

510. The rescuer, standing waist deep in the water, supports the patient face upwards in the horizontal position. Standing at his side and facing the patient's head, the rescuer reaches across with his outside hand, grasps the patient's far wrist and carries his arm across his own shoulders. At the same time the rescuer passes his other hand round the patient's body and grips his shoulder. The rescuer then turns his back to the patient, releases the grip on his wrist, and with this hand gathers in the patient's legs at the knees. By dipping in the water as necessary the patient is firmly clamped in the hollow of the rescuer's back, and the hand gripping the shoulder is moved to support the patient's neck close to the shoulders. When wading ashore the rescuer should lean forward from the hips so that the patient's weight is supported by the rescuer's legs rather than his arms.

511. To lower the patient to the ground the rescuer kneels on both knees and sits back on his heels and allows the patient to roll gently to the ground.

PART SIX

THE AFTER-CARE OF A RESCUED PERSON

600. A person who has been in serious danger of his life, or has suffered severe injury, is liable to develop shock. Without proper treatment, which may necessitate blood transfusion or surgery, shock may be fatal, and its onset makes it essential that the patient should be removed to hospital with the minimum of delay. Shock may develop at once, or its onset may be delayed; for this reason it is important that a person who has suffered an experience which may give rise to shock should be placed under medical supervision even though he may appear and claim to be perfectly well.

SHOCK

601. Shock is a condition of severe depression of vital functions due to loss of body fluid and associated changes in the circulatory system, which may vary from temporary weakness of the system to its complete failure. It is outside the scope of this book to go beyond that point in discussing the various causes of shock. The treatment of shock requires expert medical attention, but the layman can help to allay its dangers by following certain rules in the care of the patient while waiting for the arrival of medical help and a means of removing him to hospital.

602. The patient is pale and his skin is cold and clammy; beads of sweat may appear on his forehead and elsewhere. His facial expression is worried, or he may have a vacant stare, and he may be restless and fidgety. His pulse is likely to be rapid, and perhaps feeble, and his breathing is rapid and shallow. The patient may complain of thirst. *Appearance of a shocked patient*

603. The patient should not be moved unless this is necessary to get him out of danger. He should be laid on his back, if conscious, with nothing extra under his head. If he is unconscious, or vomiting, he should be gently rolled into a half-prone position in which his tongue will fall forward and the vomit can run out of his mouth instead of being drawn into his lungs.

604. The patient should not be undressed, but any tight clothing round the neck, chest and waist should be loosened if this has not already been done in connection with the application of artificial respiration.

605. The patient should be covered if the weather is cold, but *no attempt* should be made to warm him by massage or the application of artificial heat in any form.

606. If the patient has no serious external injury and there is no reason to suppose that he has suffered internal injury which may necessitate surgery on his arrival in hospital, he may, if he complains of thirst, be given small quantities of water but coffee, tea, alcohol or other stimulants should *not* be given. If there are external injuries, or if internal injury is suspected, the patient should not be given anything to drink because this may necessitate delay in the application of treatment on arrival in hospital if such treatment involves surgery and the use of anaesthetics.

607. When caring for a patient suffering from shock the life-saver must display quiet confidence. He must be careful not to discuss the patient's condition unless well out of earshot.

608. The condition of shock referred to above must not be confused with electric shock which is referred to elsewhere in this book.

CRAMP

609. Cramp, although painful, need not be dangerous when developed by a swimmer provided that he does not panic. If it does occur the swimmer should immediately signal for help, and then float on his back, or paddle gently towards safety, trailing the affected limb. He may be able to stretch and massage the affected muscle himself, but he should nevertheless signal for help.

610. Cramp is caused by the sudden contraction of a muscle, and is usually located in the lower limbs. It is liable to be brought on by:

(*a*) cold conditions,

(*b*) sudden muscular exertion,

(*c*) nervous shock,

(*d*) a blow or injury to a muscle,

(*e*) bathing or swimming too soon after a meal, or when hungry.

611. On reaching the shore the affected part should be thoroughly dried and massaged, and the muscle should be gently extended. If the cramp persists heat should be applied to the affected muscle. A victim of persistent abdominal cramps should seek medical advice without delay.

ARTIFICIAL RESPIRATION

700. Artificial respiration is the essential first aid treatment required by the victim of any accident which restricts the amount of oxygen available to the body and this treatment must be applied without an instant's delay because, once the oxygen supply is cut off the central nervous system quickly suffers damage from which it cannot be revived and the heart ceases to beat effectively. Consideration of these circumstances give rise to the following:

Golden Rules

1. *Keep calm.*
2. *Waste no time.*
3. *Decide the method of artificial respiration to be used, start to apply it immediately, and continue until self breathing is restored.*

PHYSIOLOGICAL AND ANATOMICAL CONSIDERATION

By Dr. W. D. W. Brooks, C.B.E., D.M., F.R.C.P.

701. The object of the Royal Life Saving Society is to train persons how, in an emergency, to save lives. To do this some knowledge of human anatomy and physiology is desirable; for, only if the essentials of the structure and the working of the body are understood can intelligent efforts be made to restore normal function again when through an accident the victim is near to death. Knowledge of relevant anatomy and physiology enables a trained rescuer to act on his own initiative and with authority in an emergency. He will know, for example, not only how to carry out artificial respiration, but why it is urgent, why it may be effective or ineffective, and why and what modifications must be made to suit the needs of the situation.

702. Though the components of the human body are linked in structure and in function, for our purpose the most important are those concerned with respiration, the circulation of the blood, and to a less extent those concerned with nutrition.

Respiration

703. The mouth, nose, and pharynx constitute the beginning of both the respiratory and alimentary tracts. Below the pharynx these tracts divide, air passing through the glottis into the larynx and downwards through the trachea (windpipe); food and fluid pass down the oesophagus (gullet) and thus into the stomach. The root of the tongue, the epiglottis and the vocal cords constitute a delicate mobile valvular mechanism whereby the respiratory system may be shut off on swallowing; and on the other hand, the gullet may also be closed during breathing. It is important to remember that when consciousness is clouded or lost these mechanisms often break down. In these circumstances fluid, food, or vomit may be inhaled; alternately the tongue may fall back and obstruct breathing. To prevent these happenings is a major factor in effective artificial respiration.

704. The larynx and below it the trachea are situated in the front of the neck and may be felt as hard structures there. The trachea, strengthened and kept open by C-shaped rings of cartilage passes down into the two main bronchi. These bronchi subdivide, repeatedly to supply the two lungs. All the larger bronchi, like the trachea have rings of cartilage in their walls, but as they by division become smaller their walls gradually lose their cartilage and come to contain increasing proportions of muscular and elastic tissues whereby their cross-section and length may be altered during respiration. The peripheral branches, *Larynx and trachea* *The bronchi* *Bronchioles*

53

called bronchioles, as they in turn subdivide, gradually lose their muscle until in the terminal branches little or no muscle remains and the elastic tubes end in the alveoli or air sacs. The trachea, bronchi, and bronchioles are all lined with ciliated epithelium which is kept moist by glands which excrete sputum. The ciliae lash this sputum continually upward over the glottis and there it is either swallowed or coughed out. Particles of inhaled dust trapped in this sputum are thus excreted. Each bronchiole terminates in a series of minute very thin-walled elastic sacs, called alveoli, and these ultimately receive the inspired air. They are each closely covered by a network of fine capillaries which fill with venous blood from the right ventricle of the heart through terminal branches of the pulmonary artery, and from them the blood flows back through tributaries of the pulmonary vein to the left auricle and so into the left ventricle of the heart, whence it is expelled as arterial blood throughout the body. In passing through the alveolar capillary network the blood is in close contact with the air in the alveoli, and readily gives off most of its carbon dioxide to this air, and receives from it a fresh supply of oxygen.

Alveoli

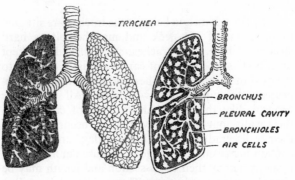

Illustration No. 16.

54

705. Each lung contains many thousands of these The lungs
alveoli which fill and are emptied of air during breathing. The lungs' movements are passive, and being
elastic organs they follow the changes in the capacity
of the chest brought about by the muscles of respiration. In inspiration the chest expands because the
diaphragm—a large muscle crossing the body at the

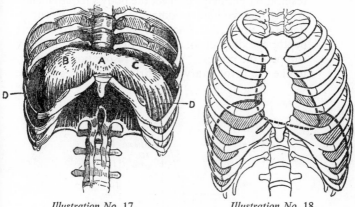

Illustration No. 17.   *Illustration No.* 18.

A. Control ⎫
B. Right ⎬ tendinous layer of diaphragm
C. Left ⎭
D. Muscular portions of diaphragm

base of the chest—moves downwards as its fibres
contract, and at the same time the ribs are raised and
moved outwards by a series of muscles called the
external intercostals. Expiration normally is a passive
act accomplished when these muscles relax by the
elastic recoil of the chest wall and of the lungs. It may
be assisted in forced expiration by contraction of
many muscles of which the internal intercostal muscles
and the muscles in the abdominal wall are the most
important. The latter by compressing the abdominal
contents force the diaphragm upwards and so dimin-
ishes the capacity of the chest.

55

706. Normal respiration is an involuntary act of which we are usually unaware, and it proceeds without fatigue in waking and sleeping throughout our lives. The volume and rate vary in different individuals and in any individual at different times; both fall during sleep, and rise with emotion, or exertion, or indeed whenever there arises the need for increased respiratory exchange to meet the body's requirements. At any time voluntary control may, at will, be superimposed upon this unconscious reflex act, altering depth, speeding up or slowing down, or temporarily stopping the process. Voluntary respiration, however, unlike the involuntary act fairly soon causes fatigue.

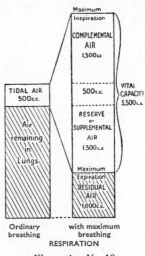

Illustration No. 19

707. The volume of the air in each breath at rest is known as the tidal volume and in an adult is approximately 500 cubic centimetres. At the end of such an

56

expiration there remains behind in the lungs about 2,500 c.c., of which approximately 1,500 c.c. may be breathed out by forced expiration, leaving a residual air which cannot be breathed out of about 1,000 c.c. Further, after breathing in the tidal air of 500 c.c. it is possible by forced inspiration to breath in a further 1,500 c.c. to fill the lungs to their maximum, and at that stage a maximum expiration (vital capacity) of about 3,500 c.c. can be made. All these values vary in different individuals but they illustrate the range of respiration of which the body is capable. A comparable variability also applies to speed of respiration, so that by both methods when the need arises a great increase in the volume of air breathed per unit of time is possible.

The Blood

708. The body's needs as regards respiration are transmitted through the nervous system, and that in turn in this respect is controlled in part by the composition of the circulating blood. To understand this it is necessary to digress. Every cell in the body needs energy to live, to grow, and to perform its specialised functions. This energy is obtained ultimately from the Energy food and fluids we take in. These are modified by digestion in the alimentary tract, absorbed, modified further in the liver and elsewhere, and the products are carried in the blood to the cells of the tissues, and there they are stored or used quickly (depending on the local activity at the time) to supply the energy needed. The energy itself arises as a result of the combustion (metabolism) of these products of our food within the cells, and for that combustion oxygen is essential—just as it is for the combustion of coal in a fire, or of petrol in a motor engine. Apart from energy liberated in the cells the waste products of this combustion pass back into the blood stream, and of

3

these carbon dioxide is got rid of by the lungs in the expired air, and other substances by the kidneys in the urine. The blood at any time therefore carries (1) the

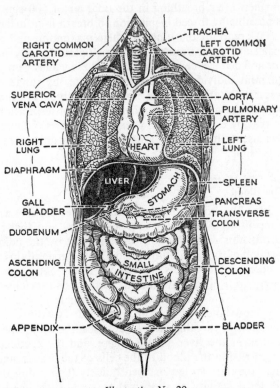

RIGHT COMMON CAROTID ARTERY

TRACHEA

LEFT COMMON CAROTID ARTERY

SUPERIOR VENA CAVA

AORTA

PULMONARY ARTERY

RIGHT LUNG

HEART

LEFT LUNG

DIAPHRAGM

LIVER

STOMACH

SPLEEN

GALL BLADDER

PANCREAS

TRANSVERSE COLON

DUODENUM

ASCENDING COLON

SMALL INTESTINE

DESCENDING COLON

APPENDIX

BLADDER

Illustration No. 20

modified products of our food which nourish all the cells of the body; (2) the waste products of the metabolism of these cells; (3) oxygen; and (4) a variety of other substances with which we are not concerned. The blood consists of a clear yellow protein-containing fluid called plasma, in which the nutrient materials to the tissue cells, and carbon dioxide, and other waste products are dissolved, and living cells called blood corpuscles in suspension. The great majority of these blood corpuscles are dark red because they contain haemoglobin—a complex organic compound containing iron. This compound combines in the capillaries around the alveoli loosely with oxygen (to give oxyhaemoglobin which is bright red in colour), and in due course this oxygen is released when later the arterial blood reaches the tissue cells of the body. On the other hand, carbon dioxide deriving from the tissue cells' metabolism is released from the plasma when the venous blood again returns to the alveolar capillaries and is discharged into the air within these lung sacs and is so breathed out. Inspired air from the atmosphere contains about 79% nitrogen, 21% oxygen, and a trace only of carbon dioxide; this mixes on inspiration in the air passages and alveoli with the contained air which by the passage of blood through the alveolar capillaries has come to contain considerably less oxygen and much more carbon dioxide; so that, when breathed out the mixture's composition is approximately 17% oxygen, 4% carbon dioxide, and 79% nitrogen. In the aggregate, therefore, in the lungs oxygen is taken up and carbon dioxide is excreted; while in the tissues oxygen is taken up and carbon dioxide is discharged. Certain centres in the nervous system are sensitive to the levels of carbon dioxide and oxygen in the circulating blood. They respond, for example, to a rise of carbon dioxide or fall of oxygen which would occur following exertion, by sending out impulses which increase the rate and depth of respiration and so correct the abnormality.

The Circulation

709. Clearly, for such a mechanism to succeed, a continuous circulation of blood through the lungs and

through the tissues is essential. The blood flows in a closed system of vessels of which there are three main types, the arteries, the capillaries, and the veins. The arteries, in which the blood flow is away from the heart, have relatively thick elastic and muscular walls. These walls permit distension, and yet maintain as a

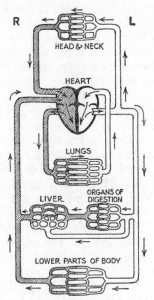

Illustration No. 21.

result of their muscles' tonic contraction a sustained pressure on the blood within them. The arteries branch repeatedly, and thus become smaller in spreading out from the heart, and the pressure within them falls off as they become smaller. They supply every tissue and organ of the body, and the finest peripheral twigs terminate in the capillaries. These are microscopic, very numerous, very thin-walled vessels which though they contain no muscle in their walls are con- Capillaries tractile so that blood flow may be diverted according to local tissue needs. The thinness of their walls permits the free passage of fluids, oxygen, and some dissolved substances to and from the cells of the tissues they supply. The capillaries are arranged in a complicated network whose structure conforms with that of the tissue in which they are situated, and gradually uniting again they are collected together into the smallest veins. The veins return the blood to Veins the heart, and grow larger as they receive more and more tributaries as they approach that organ. Their walls, though thin as compared with the corresponding arteries, once again contain muscle and elastic tissue, and in addition many veins have valves aptly sited along their length which allow the blood only to flow towards the heart.

The Heart

710. The heart is a hollow muscular pump whereby the blood is kept circulating through this system of blood vessels. It is a double pump, each half being Structure separated from the other by a septum through which there is normally no communicating passage. In each half there are two chambers, an auricle with relatively thin walls, and below it a thick-walled ventricle. Each auricle communicates with its corresponding ventricle by an opening which is furnished with a valve which allows blood to pass from auricle to ventricle but prevents its return. The two auricles contract together Action of and thus force blood into the then relaxed ventricles; the heart these in turn then contract together and force their contained blood the right into the pulmonary artery, the left into the aorta. Blood is prevented from returning from these arteries into the ventricles by valves situated at the base of each artery, so that each artery

61

remains full of blood. Thus, with each ventricular contraction a wave or pulse is sent out through the pulmonary and sytemic arterial system carrying blood respectively to the furthermost tissues of the lungs and the body. Following the ventricular contraction there ensues a passive dilation of the chambers of the heart, and then a pause during which the auricles fill with blood again, and the cardiac cycle which takes about

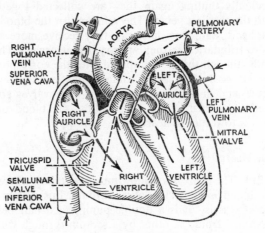

Illustration No. 22.

eight-tenths of a second is then once more repeated. These rhythmical spontaneous contractions become faster during, for example, exertion or emotion, and slower during sleep. The terminal veins from the body are two, the superior vena cava draining the head neck and arms, and the inferior vena cava from the trunk and legs. Both these veins open into the right auricle, so that their venous blood passes thence into the right ventricle whence it is expelled into the pulmonary artery and so distributed to the lungs. Here, as has been explained, it picks up oxygen and loses carbon dioxide in the alveolar capillaries and so becomes arterial in character. Arterial blood then returns from the lungs via the pulmonary veins into the left auricle, thence to the left ventricle, whence it is forced out into the aorta and so through the systemic arteries to the body tissues. A given portion of the blood completes this whole journey from the right side of the heart and back again to the same point in about half a minute, and in so doing traverses two sets of arteries, capillaries, and veins.

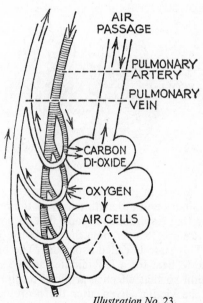

AIR PASSAGE

PULMONARY ARTERY

PULMONARY VEIN

CARBON DI-OXIDE

OXYGEN

AIR CELLS

Illustration No. 23.

Asphyxia

711. For life to be maintained continued efficient circulation of the blood is essential, and so also is efficient respiration. The failure of either affects first and most the highly sensitive and vulnerable tissues and these are the brain and spinal cord which contain

63

the centres controlling respiration and cardiac action. Thus, as in drowning, if the air supply to the lungs is obstructed by water in the air passage and alveoli, or by spasm of the glottis or by both these, the oxygen in the alveoli rapidly becomes reduced and the carbon dioxide increased so that the circulating blood takes up too little oxygen and gives off too little carbon

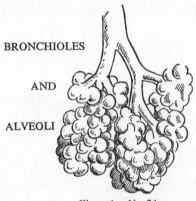

BRONCHIOLES

AND

ALVEOLI

Illustation No. 24.

dioxide. Blood in this state passing to the brain first overstimulates and at length paralyses the respiratory centre so that respirations become first deep and rapid (in an attempt to overcome the disability) and later cease. This state is called asphyxia. The heart may continue to beat for a few minutes after cessation of respiration so that effective artificial respiration may restore the victim. Even after the heart has ceased beating a fatal outcome is not certain for a further short period of time and external cardiac massage combined with artificial respiration may restore life. There are known to exist more complicated changes associated with drowning, depending on whether the water inhaled by the victim is sea-water or fresh-water, and whether shock exists, but these changes in no way alter the urgent need for artificial respiration, and if the heart has stopped, external cardiac massage in the treatment of the patient. The most commonly encountered causes of asphyxia are drowning, strangulation, and electric shock, the last of which may directly paralyse the respiratory centre and so stop respiration. For all these artificial respiration efficiently applied from an early stage may prevent a fatality.

THE MECHANICS OF BREATHING

712. The following paragraphs give a very much simplified version of the foregoing section on Physiological and Anatomical considerations. They are intended for use by young candidates for Elementary and Intermediate Certificates and the Bronze Medallion

713. It is not necessary to know medical terms and details in order to apply artificial respiration effectively, but you must understand what you are trying to do, why it is necessary and how the various methods described in the *Handbook* achieve it.

714. The human body is a complicated machine which, like all machines, must be kept supplied with a source of energy to keep it going. A motor-car must have petrol and an electric train must have electric current; without these both will stop. Similarly the human body must have air, food and drink. If any of these are completely cut off the body will die sooner or later. The human body can survive comparatively long periods without food or drink, but if its air supply is stopped death will follow in a matter of minutes. Artificial respiration is a way of supplying air to the body when an accident, such as drowning,

has prevented it getting its air supply in the ordinary way. Applied effectively and immediately, artificial respiration can often save a life which will be lost without it.

715. In artificial respiration we are concerned with the *Lungs*, which draw fresh air into the body and expel used air, the *Blood*, which carries oxygen to those parts of the body which require it, and the *Heart*, which pumps the blood round the body.

716. Air enters the body by the nose and the mouth and passes down the windpipe to the lungs. As food and drink are also taken in by the mouth there is a valve system in the throat which prevents food and liquid going into the lungs instead of the stomach. When a person is unconscious or semi-conscious this valve may not work properly. This is the reason why it is necessary to turn a patient onto his side or face immediately if he shows signs of being sick so that the vomit will run out of his mouth, and not down into his lungs where it may kill him. Similarly if consciousness is clouded or lost completely, the tongue may fall back, block the windpipe and so prevent air reaching the lungs. This is why the patient's head *must* be put in the right position as described in the various methods of artificial respiration. It is no good trying to get air into the patient's body if it cannot get into his lungs where it is required.

717. In the lungs oxygen is extracted from the air which has been breathed in and is transferred to the blood. At the same time the blood gives off carbon-dioxide which is discharged from the lungs in the act of breathing out. Thus the continuous cycle of breathing in and out keeps the blood supplied with oxygen and removes unwanted carbon dioxide which is collected up by the blood in its passage round the body.

718. The heart is a pump which circulates the blood round the body continuously. It consists of four compartments. The two upper compartments are each connected to their corresponding lower compartments by a valve which allows blood to flow from the upper compartment to the lower compartment, but prevents it flowing in the reverse direction.

719. Blood which has received oxygen from the lungs is drawn into the top left-hand compartment which then contracts and squeezes the blood into the lower left-hand compartment. The lower compartment then contracts and forces the blood out into the arteries which carry the blood away from the heart to all parts of the body. This is shown diagrammatically on page 62. The arteries branch repeatedly and as they do so become smaller and smaller. When they reach the extremities they are minute in size.

720. The veins collect up the blood after it has given up its oxygen and picked up carbon dioxide from the tissues and carry it back to the heart. Their arrangement is similar to that of the arteries. At the extremities they are also minute, and they become larger as they carry more blood and get nearer the heart. The blood carried back in the veins flows into the top right-hand compartment of the heart. From there it passes into the lower right-hand compartment which contracts in its turn and pushes the blood into an artery which carries it to the lungs. Here it gives up carbon dioxide, picks up a fresh supply of oxygen and returns to the top left-hand compartment of the heart ready to start the cycle over again. The cycle described above takes about half a minute.

721. The muscular actions which enable air to be breathed into and out of the lungs, and produce the pump action of the heart are controlled by nerve

67

centres in the brain and the spine. These centres very quickly cease to work if the blood sent to them by the heart does not contain enough oxygen. If the brain does not get enough oxygen it first of all tries to speed up the breathing, just as it does if you swim very fast and get out of breath. If the air supply to the lungs has been cut off this does no good, the nerve centre in the brain becomes paralysed and breathing ceases. This state is called asphyxia. The heart may continue to beat for a few minutes after breathing has ceased, and if air can be got into the lungs during this time by the application of artificial respiration the life of the patient may be saved.

722. In the manual method of artificial respiration the operator presses down on the patient's lungs and forces air out of them. He then moves the patient's arms in such a way that his chest will be expanded and fresh air will be drawn into the lungs. In the Expired Air method the operator blows his own expired air, which still contains an adequate amount of oxygen, directly into the patient's lungs and the residual elasticity of the patient's muscles deflates them.

723. The Expired Air method is more effective than the manual method and should always be used when circumstances permit.

THE FIRST AID APPLICATION OF ARTIFICIAL RESPIRATION

724. To many people mention of artificial respiration at once brings to mind the treatment of the near-drowned, but as a first aid measure it may equally be required for the treatment of other conditions encountered in everyday life, some frequently and others less frequently. These conditions are listed below; each one is an *emergency* and calls for *immediate action* before professional assistance is available. Although

in some cases artificial respiration is only a part of the first aid treatment required, its immediate application may be the means of saving life.

725. The conditions which may call for artificial respiration as a first aid measure in an emergency are:

(*a*) Drowning.

(*b*) Coal-gas poisoning.

(*c*) Poisoning by gases other than coal-gas.

(*d*) Electric shock and the effects of lightning.

(*e*) Suffocation, hanging, and strangulation.

(*f*) A foreign body in the throat.

726. The changes which occur in the body in the above conditions vary considerably but there is one common feature, namely the lack of oxygen in the arterial blood; if this is of sufficient degree and sufficiently prolonged it will produce death if not remedied. Artificial respiration must be given without delay when a victim of one of the above conditions is not apparently breathing or if the breathing is so shallow that it cannot be seen at a glance. This very shallow breathing is usually at a slower rate than normal which, in the case of a sleeping or resting person, may be only about ten times per minute. No harm will result if the victim is given artificial respiration when in fact he is breathing slowly or imperceptibly, but once started artificial respiration must be continued without stopping until the normal rhythm and depth of breathing is restored.

727. There is no need to apply artificial respiration if the victim is able to talk, cry or shout; if, in fact, he is conscious. The restoration of spontaneous breathing is the desired point; beyond this it is unnecessary to apply further treatment. There is no need to continue until animation is apparent.

728. In some cases the victim will be dead before artificial respiration is started or he will die during its application, but owing to the inability of the ordinary person to assess this state the operator must continue to apply artificial respiration until someone competent to determine whether death has occurred arrives. Sometimes the operator will be the only person on the spot and he will have no means of summoning help. How long to continue artificial respiration in these circumstances is a difficult problem which is discussed separately below; it is sufficient to say here that the time during which an operator may have to give artificial respiration without assistance may be prolonged.

729. The emergencies in which artificial respiration may be required are considered in more detail below. In each case a brief description of the appearance of the victim is given but, normally, the circumstances of the incident alone will be sufficient to determine instantly the nature of the condition to be treated.

DROWNING

Appearance

730. The face and particularly the lips and ears of the victim may be various shades of dark purple. There may be a fine foam-like froth issuing from the mouth and nostrils.

Treatment

731. It used to be taught that the mouth should be cleared of obstructions such as weed and false teeth; also the victim was held head downwards to drain the water from the air passage and the lungs. Nowadays it is realised that the time interval is very short in which successful resuscitation can be achieved, and even seconds must not be wasted. It is the froth in the small airways in the lungs which obstructs the passage of air and this froth cannot be removed. The water does not prevent air getting into the lungs and time must not be wasted in an endeavour to get rid of it.

732. What must be done is:

(*a*) The Expired Air method of artificial respiration should be commenced as soon as the rescuer can get his feet on firm ground whilst still in the water and should be continued whilst wading ashore with the victim. It is important that this initial exchange of air should be given as early as possible and before moving the victim to a more suitable position lying on his back on firm ground. In the case of drowning the mouth-to-nose technique is preferred as being less likely to cause the patient to vomit.

(*b*) If one of the manual methods is to be used, the victim must be removed from the water as quickly as possible and, for the Silvester-Brosch method, placed on his back with a pad under his shoulders, or, for, the Holger Nielsen method, placed face downwards with his head resting on his hands, face to one side. In the Expired Air and Silvester-Brosch methods it is of advantage to have the victim's head higher than his stomach as, in this position, fluid is more likely to remain in the stomach. If there is any obvious obstruction to the airway, it should be quickly removed, but do not try to examine the mouth or throat thoroughly, thereby wasting valuable time. Tight clothing round the neck and chest should be loosened.

(*c*) Begin artificial respiration at once by whatever method you know. Don't wait to examine the victim; if he is breathing normally so as not to require artificial respiration this will have been obvious while placing him on the ground.

(*d*) Continue artificial respiration *without stopping* for at least half an hour unless recovery takes place before that time has elapsed. Remember that time passes slowly in an emergency and that what sometimes appears to be a long time is in fact only a few minutes. The dark purple of the lips and ears and the duskiness of the face should change quickly to the normal colour— or perhaps paler than normal due to chill—if the victim is alive and artificial respiration is proving effective. If you have received proper and thorough training in External Cardiac Compression, or there is someone else present who has received such instruction, you should feel the carotid pulse in the victim's neck after a few breaths with the Expired Air method. If this cannot be felt you should immediately combine cardiac compression with artificial respiration by the Expired Air method. (See paragraph 763.)

733. Recovery will be indicated by the obvious return of normal deep breathing, struggling or vocal demonstration, but this does not necessarily imply return to full consciousness. If the victim has not recovered, artificial respiration must be continued until a qualified authority arrives. The importance of continuous artificial respiration, and particularly the need for starting without an instant's delay cannot be overstressed.

734. When the operator is alone and no assistance or advice is forthcoming it is advisable to continue artificial respiration for at least one hour, and no harm can come from continuing beyond this time.

735. When using the manual method, no attempt must be made to move the victim into an ambulance or to put him on a stretcher during the first half hour unless obvious recovery has taken place. No interference with artificial respiration must be permitted during the vital period before the restoration of normal breathing, but when using the Expired Air method it is possible, with careful thought, to continue artificial respiration whilst the victim is being moved.

736. The victim should be covered with any available covering to prevent his becoming chilled *provided that* bystanders are available to do this and that it does not interfere with the rhythm of artificial respiration. If possible in the same conditions the victim should be dried but on the whole it is preferable not to attempt to remove wet clothing if the victim is dressed—protection from the wind by covering will suffice.

737. When normal breathing has been restored the patient may still remain unconscious. He should not be left alone in this condition in case respiration fails again. He should be turned on his side in case he vomits.

COAL GAS POISONING

738. This may be accidental or suicidal. The first aid treatment is that for coal-gas poisoning, but the victim may also have taken a sleeping drug so that unconsciousness may be due either to the gas or a drug. In coal-gas poisoning unconsciousness is caused by the pigment of the blood uniting with carbon monoxide in the coal gas thereby preventing the normal combination of the pigment with oxygen. The brain is deprived of its oxygen supply and if the condition is severe or prolonged the respiratory centre of the brain, which controls breathing, ceases to work, breathing stops and death follows. It is for this reason that artificial respiration must be given without delay if breathing is shallow or imperceptible. Recovery from the effects of coal-gas poisoning is much slower than that from the effects of near-drowning and artificial respiration may have to be continued for much longer periods before normal breathing is restored. Treatment is directed to keeping the blood as fully oxygenated as possible by maintaining adequate respiration. Whenever possible, pure oxygen should be administered but this is seldom available at once.

Appearance

739. The face of the victim will probably appear flushed with an abnormally pink or rouge-like flush. Breathing may be shallow or imperceptible.

First Aid Treatment

740. The steps to be taken are:

(a) Remove the victim from the gas contaminated area into the fresh air. Do not use naked lights to facilitate search for or removal of the victim.

(b) Start artificial respiration immediately. Traces of coal-gas from the patient may make the use of the Expired Air method unsuitable in which case the manual method should be used. Recovery will be slow if the victim is really in need of artificial respiration and it must be continued until normal breathing is restored.

Other Similar Forms of Poisoning

741. The effects of coal-gas poisoning and its treatment have been mentioned separately, but the same instructions apply to poisoning arising from the exhaust fumes of a car, inefficient ventilation from a defective gas geyser and when stoves, particularly coke stoves, are improperly used. All are essentially carbon monoxide poisoning. Carbon monoxide itself is odourless, but there may be fumes from other substances present. Persons being poisoned in these ways may experience giddiness, drowsiness, faintness, palpitation and nausea. They will recover on removing themselves to outside fresh air. Artificial respiration is not required in carbon monoxide poisoning if the sufferer is conscious.

POISONING BY GASES OTHER THAN COAL-GAS

742. Under this heading are included a variety of circumstances which may lead to fatalities. Although this end may be brought about in different ways, all ultimately involve lack of oxygenation of the blood supply. Examples commonly met with are:

(*a*) Persons overcome by irritant fumes which produce an inflammation of the lungs. This results in inadequate oxygen transfer in the lungs with an eventual failure of respiration, at which stage artificial respiration is called for, preferably with the added application of pure oxygen if available. These circumstances may arise in industrial accidents when, for example, ammonia containers burst.

(*b*) **Oxygen lack.** This may occur in compartments which are not ventilated or opened up except at long intervals. In such compartments it is possible for the oxygen in the enclosed air to be absorbed by painted surfaces or to be used up in the rusting of metallic surfaces. Examples are in double bottoms of ships and underground tanks. Immediate artificial respiration in fresh air is called for.

> Warning. Compartments such as these should be entered only by rescuers wearing a breathing apparatus which has its own air or oxygen supply, either self-contained or through a hose or pipe the other end of which is in fresh air. A handkerchief over the nose or a "gas mask" gives *no protection* against oxygen lack, carbon monoxide or carbon dioxide.

(*c*) **Poisoning by various gases.** Some gases are in themselves poisonous, for example, Cyanogen which is used for killing vermin and which poisons the cells of the nervous system.

743. Although carbon dioxide is normally present in the air in small concentration and a function of the respiratory system is to remove this gas from the body, a sufficient concentration of carbon dioxide will have a paralysing effect on the centres of the brain which control breathing, and death can occur rapidly in exposure to a high concentration.

744. Nerve gases, which might be used in war, cause rapid respiratory paralysis and call for the immediate application of artificial respiration.

745. Sewer-gas and Mine-gas poisoning are examples of poisoning under everyday circumstances. The picture may be a mixed one comprising lack of oxygen, poisoning by carbon dioxide, methane, carbon monoxide and sulphuretted hydrogen; these gases each produce their specific effects but the treatment required is to produce adequate oxygenation of the blood by the application of artificial respiration in fresh air.

ELECTRIC SHOCK

(including the effects of lightning)

746. The reaction of the human body to electric current passing through it is complex and variable, but in general two effects are produced; a local burn is caused in the area adjacent to the point of contact and more remote injury may occur giving rise to unconsciousness and interference with the muscle control of respiration. Generally speaking the extent of injury is in proportion to the efficiency of the victim as a conductor between the electric circuit and "earth"; it follows that the risk of fatal shock is greater when the clothing and shoes are wet, and particularly when any part of the body is immersed in water, as when taking a bath or washing in a hand basin. Lightning may produce bizarre effects, frequently stripping clothing into shreds.

747. A victim of electric shock must be disconnected from the current, but in doing so the rescuer must himself avoid being shocked. If it is not possible to break the circuit by switching it off or disconnecting it, the victim should be pushed away from the conductor by using a piece of dry wood or other non-conducting material ; if these are not immediately available the victim should be pulled away with a loop of rope, or by grasping a dry part of his own clothing but *not* any part of his flesh. The risk to the rescuer will be less if he is wearing dry or rubber-shod boots or shoes. In some circumstances as a last resort it may be possible to disconnect the victim by the use of a flying tackle, rugby football fashion, but if this method is employed it must be done vigorously so that the rescuer is completely airborne at the time when he is himself in contact with the electric current through the victim. When the victim has grasped a live conductor, it may be that his grip cannot be released. Such a situation is most likely to arise at a switchboard or in connection with a large piece of electrical equipment. If the circuit cannot be broken by normal arrangements, an attempt may be made to throw a piece of metal or other conducting material across the circuit to cause a short-circuit and the blowing of a fuse at a distant point.

748. First aid treatment is essentially artificial respiration if the victim is not apparently breathing naturally. Unconsciousness will probably be present and the face of the victim may appear congested and purple due to inability to oxygenate the blood supply by adequate respiration. Artificial respiration may be needed for hours, and should be continued until a doctor arrives or until the victim has obviously re- covered consciousness or normal breathing.

749. In his annual report some years ago the Chief Inspector of Factories referred to thirteen cases of successful resuscitation from the effects of electric shock, and went on to say "as these cases may be regarded as potential fatalities, and represent only a proportion of the accidents in which artificial respiration could and should have been attempted, the importance of inculcating a knowledge of the technique as widely as possible needs no emphasis."

750. Burns resulting from contact with an electric circuit may be severe. No attempt should be made to remove the clothing adhering to the burn, but if other help is available, or as soon as artificial respiration is no longer required, the wound should be covered with a drying dressing. Oil or grease in any form should *not* be applied.

OTHER CONDITIONS REQUIRING ARTIFICIAL RESPIRATION

Suffocation, Hanging and Strangulation

751. These conditions, which may occur accidentally, are not uncommon. The victims suffer lack of oxygenation of the blood and failure of respiration. The urgent need is the removal of the mechanical obstruction to breathing and the immediate application of artificial respiration.

Foreign Body in the Throat

752. Most people are familar with the appearance produced when a foreign body becomes stuck in the throat. The face of the victim becomes congested and purple, the lips becoming very dark coloured. Violent attempts at respiration are made, with perhaps grunting and strident inspiratory efforts. Retching may be present. The obstruction to breathing is caused not so much by the foreign body itself, but by the spasm of the muscles of the throat which close the structures tightly round the offending object, thereby narrowing or obliterating the air passage. Initially treatment should be directed to the removal of the foreign body. If large, it may be possible to remove it with the fingers. If no obstruction can be seen, the tongue should be pulled forward, the head bent forward and a hearty smack given between the shoulder blades; this may or may not jerk the throat sufficiently for the object to be dislodged and spat out. As long as the victim is making violent efforts to take a breath there is no point in giving artificial respiration, and efforts to locate and remove the object should continue. In general the victim should be placed in a prone position, the face resting on the hands. If possible the body should rest head down on a slope; this position tends to prevent any object entering the trachea and lessens the risk of vomit entering the trachea should vomiting occur, which is very possible. Unconsciousness will supervene if the airway is completely obstructed. Relaxation of the spasm may occur with unconsciousness, in which case the airway may be restored. Artificial respiration must be started immediately if the victim's own respiration begins to fail when in the unconscious state.

CIRCUMSTANCES IN WHICH THE MANUAL METHOD IS ADVISABLE

753. Whilst the Society has chosen the Expired Air method as the preferred method of artificial respiration, there may be circumstances under which it is not possible for this method to be used. Amongst these circumstances are:

(a) Aesthetic objections on the part of the operator;

(b) Facial injuries to the victim;

(c) Victim trapped in the face downwards position;

(d) Victim's face contaminated with poisonous agricultural spray.

In these cases, and others where the Expired Air method cannot be used, the manual method must be used and it is important that all life-savers should have practical knowledge of the Silvester-Brosch method.

THE EXPIRED AIR METHOD OF ARTIFICIAL RESPIRATION

754. This method of artificial respiration is more effective than the manual methods because, whilst it has the same advantage in that it can be carried out by a single operator, it produces better ventilation of the lungs than the manual methods. Whatever method is used, it is essential that artificial respiration be given as quickly as possible.

Other advantages of the method are:

(a) It is easy to teach, even to children.

(b) It is easier for children to perform on adults than the manual methods.

(c) It can be commenced at an earlier stage in a rescue from drowning than the manual methods.

(d) Oxygen can be got into the victim's lungs faster and in greater quantities than by any other known emergency method of artificial respiration.

(e) The victim is in the supine position should external cardiac compression be required and available from trained medical personnel.

(*f*) Both hands of the rescuer are free to ensure a clear airway.

(*g*) The rescuer is in a position to observe the victim's face, see the chest rise and hear the air being exhaled.

(*h*) No special apparatus is required.

In certain circumstances it *may* be possible to commence expired air resuscitation whilst swimming with the patient but this depends on water conditions and the respective sizes of rescuer and patient. The rescuer may only succeed in further submerging the patient. If a few breaths can be given they can be of great value but time should not be lost in trying if it is not immediately successful. The value of these breaths is in oxygenating the blood flowing to the brain of the patient. As soon as the rescuer can place his feet firmly on the bottom it is possible to commence the method. This initial exchange of air should be carried out before taking the patient from the water and placing him in a more desirable position on land. The water will help to support the patient's body.

The patient should be positioned, if time permits, with his head higher than his stomach as, in this position, any fluid is more likely to remain in the stomach. If the patient vomits he should be turned at once on to his side so as far as possible to prevent the inhalation of vomit.

Should gurgling noises be heard the patient should be turned onto his shoulder with his head tilted back and lower than his chest.

A brief look at the patient's mouth should suffice to see whether any clearing is necessary but in the mouth-to-nose technique may not be necessary. If there is any obstruction it will become apparent with the first exhalation by the operator. Using the mouth-to-mouth technique a quick look into the mouth before making the first exhalation will disclose any obvious blockage. A slap between the shoulder blades with the patient turned face downwards, especially in children, may dislodge an obstruction in the airway. A first inflation of the lungs should normally be tried and if the chest does not rise the mouth and throat of the patient should be cleared with the finger.

In any method of artificial respiration it is essential to obtain the best possible airway to the lungs of the patient. In order to ensure this, the patient's head must have the maximum possible backwards tilt.

There will be cases in which it is not possible to carry out the expired air method and the manual method must be used. Amongst these cases are asphyxia due to insecticides, noxious gases and overdoses of corrosive poisons when direct contact with the nose or mouth of the patient would endanger the operator. It may also be impossible where there are facial injuries.

755. There are three techniques by which the method can be applied:

(a) Mouth-to-Nose

Advantages

1. The nose acts as a natural reduction valve and reduces the risk of air entering the stomach.
2. It is easy to make an airtight seal over the nose even when a child is using the method on an adult.

Disadvantage

The nose of the patient may be blocked. Although this prevents this technique being used, it does however ensure a seal for carrying out the mouth-to-mouth technique.

(b) Mouth-to-Mouth

Disadvantages

1. Opening the mouth can close the throat.

2. The greater pressure obtained makes it easier for air to enter the stomach and cause regurgitation.

3. In the case of spasms it may not be easy to open the mouth of the patient.

4. A child may find difficulty in making an effective air seal round the mouth of an adult.

(c) Mouth Covering Nose and Mouth of Patient

This technique is for use when performing the method on small children and babies, and controlled puffs must be used, ceasing as the chest starts to rise.

HOW TO CARRY OUT EXPIRED AIR RESUSCITATION

756. (*a*) Lay the patient on his back and, if on a slope, have the stomach slightly lower than the chest.

(*b*) Make a brief inspection of the mouth and throat to ensure that they are clear of obvious obstruction.

(*c*) Give the patient's head the maximum backwards tilt so that the chin is prominent, the mouth closed and the neck stretched to give a clear airway.

Illustration No. 25.   Head tilted fully backwards.

(*d*) Open your mouth wide, make an airtight seal over the nose of the patient and blow. The operator's cheek or the hand supporting the chin can be used to seal the patient's lips.

(c) *Or*, if the nose is blocked, open the patient's mouth using the hand supporting the chin, open your mouth wide and make an airtight seal over his mouth and blow. This may also be used as an alternative to

Illustration No. 26.   Mouth sealed round nose of patient.

the mouth-to-nose technique even when the nose is not blocked, in which case the nostrils must be sealed with the operator's cheek or the hand holding the top of the patient's head moved and the fingers used to pinch the nostrils. The wrist must be kept low on the patient's forehead to ensure that the full tilt of the head is maintained. If the patient's mouth cannot be opened, blow through his parted lips as the air passing between his teeth may be sufficient to inflate his lungs.

Illustration No. 27.   Mouth sealed round mouth of patient. Cheek sealing nose (or nostrils may be pinched).

(*f*) After exhaling, turn your head to watch for chest movement, whilst inhaling deeply in readiness for blowing again.

84

(*g*) If the chest does not rise, check that the patient's mouth and throat are free of obstruction and the head is tilted backwards as far as possible. Blow again.

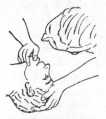

Illustration No. 28. *Watching for chest movement whilst taking a deep breath.*

(*h*) If air enters the patient's stomach through blowing too hard, press the stomach gently, with the head of the patient turned to one side.

(*j*) Commence resuscitation with four quick infla-|tions of the patient's chest to give rapid build up of oxygen in the patient's blood and then slow down to twelve to fifteen respirations per minute or blow again each time the patient's chest has deflated.

With small children and babies, inflation at the rate of twenty a minute is achieved by a series of puffs, each one ceasing as the chest starts to rise. *In no circumstances blow violently into a baby's lungs.*

(*k*) Whilst preparing to commence resuscitation breathe deeply with the mouth open to build up the oxygen content.

INSTRUCTION DRILL FOR EXPIRED AIR RESUSCITATION

757. This drill is for teaching the correct positioning of the head of the patient and the treatment up to the point of making contact, but no contact is actually made. For aesthetic and safety reasons the actual blowing of air into the "patient's" lungs is not done during training. A more complete training is given by the use of a training mask or practice on a manikin.

It is necessary that drill, when used as a method of instruction, should not be hurried so that mistakes can be seen and corrected; but the instructor should take every opportunity to impress on the class the fact that when artificial respiration is actually required in an emergency its commencement *with the absolute minimum of delay* may often be the deciding factor between success and failure in saving a life.

The class should form up in pairs, each pair being as nearly equal in size as possible; but care should be taken to leave a clear space of at least 4 feet between each pair in any line and 6 feet between each rank. This allows space for the patient to lie down and the operator to kneel beside the patient.

"In Pairs—Fall In"

Pairs fall in in line with a gap of about 4 feet between each pair. Ranks in addition to the front rank fall in behind the pairs forming the front rank with a space of 6 feet between ranks.

Should it be desired to cover the floor in order to protect the clothing of the members of the class, the Instructor will give the order: "For Resuscitation Work—Prepare."

"For Resuscitation, Class—Position"

The "patient" will kneel, and then fall forward on his hands and lying full length on the floor with his face resting on the left cheek, arms stretched above his head.

The operator moves forward simultaneously and kneels on the left by the patient's shoulder and facing the patient. He will place the patient's right arm by his side, take hold of the patient's shoulder with his left hand and the hip with the right hand, enclosing the

86

passive hand under the wrist. With a steady pull with both arms, roll the body towards him and support it against his thighs. The operator will quickly inspect the mouth and remove anything that is blocking the air passages. He will then transfer his left hand to support the patient's head and ensure that the shoulder is resting on his forearm. The right hand should loosen its grip and slide beneath the hip. When the operator has taken a fresh hold with his hands, he will adjust his kneeling position and turn the patient on to his back and bring the patient's left arm to his side.

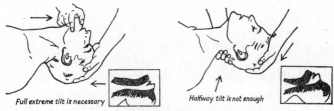

Full extreme tilt is necessary   Halfway tilt is not enough

Illustration No. 29.

Still facing the patient, the operator will move on his knees until his head is in line with the patient's head. With his right hand under the patient's neck and his left hand on top of the head he lifts the neck and tilts the head backwards as far as possible. The patient's chin is then gripped by the thumb and first two fingers of the operator's right hand. *It is essential* that the tilt is as far backwards as possible. (*Illustration No. 29.*)

Both hands are then used to ensure that the maximum tilt has been achieved. It is preferable to keep the thumb on the chin, the index finger following the line of the jaw and the remaining fingers curled into the palm so that they support the chin. *No pressure is to be exerted on the throat.*

Whilst performing these motions the operator will breathe as deeply as possible to ensure the maximum build up of oxygen in his lungs and blood stream.

"Resuscitation—Commence"

With his face at least 6 inches above that of the patient or leaning just beyond the patient's left cheek, the operator will carry out the breathing movements of expired air resuscitation for at least 1 minute. He will take a deep breath, open his mouth wide and breathe out strongly and steadily. He will then immediately turn his head to the right so that he can watch the patient's chest rise and at the same time he inhales deeply. The first four breaths must be as deep and rapid as possible after which a rate of twelve to fifteen times a minute should be maintained.

"Class—Halt. On to the Side—Turn"

On this command, to simulate dealing with vomit, the operator will raise the patient's right shoulder and so turn the upper part of the body onto its side, supporting it on his right thigh. In this position the head will be lower than the chest and the motions of clearing the mouth and throat may be shown.

"Resume Position"

On this command the operator will lower the patient onto his back, supporting the right shoulder with his right hand whilst he moves his right knee and using his left hand to support the head. He will then resume the operating position, making sure that the patient's head is given the maximum backwards tilt.

"Resuscitation—Commence"

The breathing will again be commenced at a rate of twelve to fifteen per minute for a brief period.

"Resuscitation—Halt"

On this command the operator will cease the breathing movements and stand to attention, facing front, at the side of the patient's right hip.

"Re—Form"

The operator, taking the patient's right hand in both of his own will assist him to rise and then both will resume their position in line at attention, as at the completion of the opening drill.

"Places—Change"

On the word "Change," the original operator becomes the patient and adopts the prone position as already described and the new operator moves forward and kneels on the left by the patient's shoulder. He then continues as described in "For Resuscitation, Class—Position."

NOTES FOR INSTRUCTORS

758. When the class becomes proficient at the drill, they should be encouraged to try from the opposite side, with the patient on a table and in other positions which might be encountered in a real emergency.

When a Mask or Manikin is Available

When practising with a mask or manikin, it may not be possible to carry out the first part of the drill so that practice should commence from the patient being in the supine position ready for resuscitation. The operator takes a deep breath, opens his mouth wide, makes an airtight seal round the nose of the facepiece and blows. After blowing he turns his head to the right so that he can watch the rise of the "lung," taking a deep breath whilst doing so. Practice must also be carried out with the mouth-to-mouth technique, the operator making a seal round the mouth of the facepiece and using his cheek to block the nostrils of the "dummy." To simulate nasal blockage, plugs may be put in the nostrils of the facepiece. The class should also try sealing the nostrils by pinching with the fingers of the hand holding the head. Care must be taken that full backwards tilt is maintained whilst doing this.

Practise the class in giving small puffs for babies and small children using the nose of the facepiece to represent nose *and* mouth.

Time may not permit practice in all three techniques on a manikin in which case it is most important that the class should be given the opportunity of trying the mouth-to-nose technique, which is considered to be the most effective.

EXPIRED AIR RESUSCITATION USED IN CONJUNCTION WITH EXTERNAL CARDIAC COMPRESSION

759. The Expired Air method can be used in conjunction with External Cardiac Compression and reference to this will be found in paragraph 763.

THE SILVESTER-BROSCH METHOD

760. In this method the patient is laid flat on his back and a pad (e.g. two bulky rolled towels, folded coat or folded light rug) is placed under his shoulders. The advantage of this method is that the patient is in the correct position for the application of External Cardiac Compression if required. It can also be combined with External Cardiac Compression as described in paragraph 769. The Silvester-Brosch method can be applied in a small boat if the manual method is necessary.

INSTRUCTIONAL DRILL FOR THE SILVESTER-BROSCH METHOD

761. The class falls in as described for the Expired Air method.

"For Resuscitation Class—Position"

The "patient" will kneel, and then fall forward on his hands and lie full length on the floor with his head resting on the left cheek, arms stretched above his head.

The operator will be equipped with suitable padding and will simultaneously move forward and kneel on the left side of the patient in line with the small of the back. He will place the padding in a position which he estimates will correspond with the position of the patient's shoulder blade when lying on his back. The operator then turns the patient as described in the instructional drill for the Expired Air method. When the turn has been completed, he adjusts the position of the padding. The padding should be thick enough so that the patient's head is barely touching the ground and the neck is fully extended.

The operator will move quickly to the head of the patient and kneel on the right knee which must be just clear of the top of the patient's head and in line with his right ear. The operator's left foot will be placed with the toes slightly to the left of and level with the patient's left shoulder. The operator will grasp the patient's wrists and cross

Illustration No. 30.

91

them at a point corresponding to the lower end of the patient's breast bone. (*Illustrations Nos.* 30 and 31.)

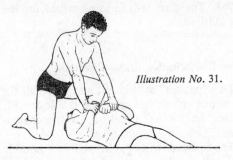

Illustration No. 31.

"Resuscitation—Commence"

One—Two

The operator rocks the weight of his trunk gently forward until his straightened arms are vertical, and by so doing, exerts a smooth, gentle, evenly increasing pressure from above, downwards on the patient's chest, using no force whatever and taking care not to bend the arms (pressure of 22 to 30 lb for an adult, 12 to 14 lb for slight women and children and 2 to 4 lb for infants is sufficient). He then rocks back releasing the pressure and lifting the patient's arms.

Three

The patient's arm movement is continued outwards and with a semi-circular sweep (*Illustration No.* 32).

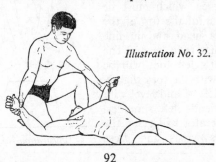

Illustration No. 32.

The movement is continued until the patient's arms are extended above his head (*Illustration No. 33*). The movement is carried out smoothly and generally parallel to the ground and is terminated as slight resistance is felt. Do not force the patient's arms to the ground when in the extended position as damage may be done.

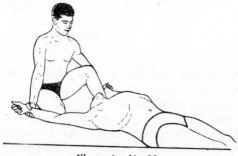

Illustration No. 33.

Four—Five

Return the patient's arms along the same route and place them in their original position on the patient's chest. Two seconds for raising arms, 2 seconds for returning, 1 second for chest pressure means that the whole cycle is being carried out twelve times a minute.

"Class—Halt"

The operator completes the cycle and stands up at attention facing the front beside the patient's right hip.

"Re—Form"

As for instructional drill for the Expired Air method

EXTERNAL CARDIAC COMPRESSION

762. From 1st September, 1967, the theory and application of External Cardiac Compression will become part of the syllabus of examination for the following awards:

Theory only	Theory and Practice
Bronze Medallion	The Instructor's Certificate
Scholar Instructor Certificate	The Award of Merit
	The Distinction Award
	The Diploma of the Society
	The Advanced Artificial Respiration Award
	The Life Guard Proficiency Test

763. External Cardiac Compression provides a means of maintaining the circulation when the heart has ceased to beat, cardiac arrest, and in favourable cases may cause the heart to start beating again. It should only be used when cardiac arrest is certain and requires precision of movement to avoid injury to the patient. External Cardiac Compression must be combined with artificial respiration as External Cardiac Compression alone does not provide adequate ventilation.

Indication

764. The indications for using External Cardiac Compression are failure to feel a pulse, femoral, radial or carotid; the pupils are or become widely dilated and the patient's colour is or becomes blue-grey and does not improve with artificial respiration.

In emergency resuscitation the first duty of an operator is to use Expired Air resuscitation. After a few breaths, if the above indications are applicable he should immediately combine External Cardiac Compression with Expired Air resuscitation.

Method

765. The patient should be placed, if possible, on a firm surface (floor or low table); if it is necessary to move the patient Expired Air resuscitation should be continued during the moving but there should be a minimum of delay in starting External Cardiac Compression, seconds are vital to its success. The operator should then kneel or stand by the side of the patient and strike the chest over the heart smartly as this may be enough to restart the heart beat.

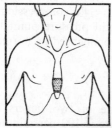 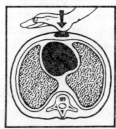

Illustration No. 45.

If there is still no response start External Cardiac Compression while continuing to ventilate the lungs. Place the heel of one hand on the lower half of the patient's sternum keeping the fingers off the chest. Place the other hand on top and with the elbows straight and a rhythmic swinging forward of the shoulders vertically compress the sternum and so squeeze the heart against the vertebral column at a rate of one compression per second. In an unconscious adult it can be depressed towards the spine for one and a half inches. Effective compression will produce a pulse, reduce the pupils in size and improve the patient's colour.

Note: IN TRAINING EXTERNAL CARDIAC COMPRESSION SHOULD NOT BE PRACTISED ON ANOTHER PERSON DUE TO THE PHYSICAL PAIN AND POSSIBLE RISK OF INJURY INVOLVED.

One Operator

766. If there is one operator only, one inflation of the lungs should be given between each five to eight

compressions. The operator, kneeling at the side of the patient, will only have to alter his position slightly to carry out both ventilation and compression.

Two Operators

767. One operator carries out External Cardiac Compression while the second gives the intermittent inflations, one inflation to five to eight compressions, and feels the pulse at the carotid pressure point to check whether the heart has recommenced its normal beat.

Infants and Young Children

768. For infants the pressure of two fingers is enough and the compression rate is 100 per minute. Sufficient support for compression can be given by placing the free hand underneath the infant's back. For children up to 10 years of age one hand is sufficient and the compression rate is 80 to 90 times per minute.

External Cardiac Compression combined with the Silvester-Brosch Method of Artificial Respiration

769. This can be carried out by applying the compressions, at the recommended rate, when the patient's hands are crossed on the sternum. As the operator kneels at the top of the head in this method it is important that he rocks forward far enough to apply vertical pressure and that the wrists are kept on the lower half of the sternum and not allowed to slip down onto the stomach.

Application

770. The pressure in all cases should be firm and controlled and applied vertically. Erratic or violent action is dangerous.

Continue External Cardiac Compression until either a definite pulse is felt in the neck or the patient is handed over to a doctor.

If the heartbeat is restarted, compression should be stopped. Artificial Respiration may be required for a considerable time after the heart starts to beat.

A patient who has required emergency resuscitation must be taken to hospital as soon as possible whether he has been revived or is still unconscious.

INSTRUCTION DRILL FOR EXTERNAL CARDIAC COMPRESSION

771. This drill is for teaching the position of the arms and the hands on the lower half of the sternum and the action to be taken up to the point of applying pressure on a live patient. A more complete training is given if a manikin is available for demonstration and practice.

It is necessary, that drill, when used as a method of instruction, should not be hurried so that mistakes can be seen and corrected; but the instructor should take every opportunity to impress on the class that when External Cardiac Compression is actually required in an emergency it must be started without delay. The use of a kitchen or bathroom scale is recommended for this drill to determine the amount of pressure applied. Where these are not available, a solid object, raised to chest level, should be used.

The class should form up in pairs, care being taken to leave a clear space of at least 4 feet between each pair in any line and 6 feet between each rank. This allows space for the patient to lie down and the operator kneel beside him.

"In Pairs—Fall In"

Pairs fall in in line with a gap of about 4 feet between each pair. Ranks in addition to the front rank fall in behind the pairs forming the front rank with a space of 6 feet between ranks.

Should it be desired to cover the floor in order to protect the clothing of the members of the class, the Instructor will give the order: "For Resuscitation Work—Prepare".

"For Resuscitation, Class—Position"

The patient will kneel and then turning will lie full length on the floor in a face upwards position with his hands at his sides.

The operator moves forward simultaneously and kneels by the patient's shoulder facing the patient. The operator will quickly inspect the patient's mouth and remove anything that is blocking the air passages. He will then place the patient's head in the extended position to receive Expired Air resuscitation. Whilst performing these motions the operator will breathe deeply to build up the oxygen content in his lungs.

"Resuscitation—Commence"

With his chin slightly higher than and beyond the patient's face, the operator will carry out the initial four deep rapid breaths of Expired Air resuscitation. He will then carefully examine the patient's pupils, feel for the carotid pulse at the neck pressure point and check the patient's colour.

The operator will then adjust his position to the side of the patient's chest, go through the motion of striking the chest and place his hands in the required position for the application of External Cardiac Compression and WITHOUT APPLYING PRESSURE position himself so that his arms become vertical over the patient's chest. After demonstrating this position by remaining still for a few seconds the operator will then reposition his hands on the scales or object placed next to the patient and apply the full cycle of resuscitation until the command to "halt" is given. The pressure required to be effective is from 55 to 70 lb in a normal adult.

"Resuscitation—Halt"

On this command the operator will cease the resuscitation movements and stand to attention, facing front, at the side of the patient's hip.

"Re-Form"

The operator, taking one of the patient's hands in both of his own will assist him to rise and then both will resume their position in line at attention, as at the completion of the opening drill.

"Places—Change"

On the word "Change", the original operator becomes the patient and adopts the supine position as already described and the new operator moves forward and kneels by the patient's shoulder. He then continues as described in "For Resuscitation, Class—Position".

PART EIGHT

THE PROFICIENCY AWARDS OF THE SOCIETY

LIFE SAVING AWARDS

800. The examinations for the proficiency awards are designed to produce a progressive standard of ability to save life from drowning. In ascending order of importance the awards are:

ELEMENTARY CERTIFICATE—a general introduction to life saving.

INTERMEDIATE CERTIFICATE—ability to make a rescue over a short distance.

UNIGRIP CERTIFICATE—proficiency in the Unigrip method of rescue.

BRONZE MEDALLION—ability to make a rescue over a longer distance and in more difficult circumstances than those envisaged in the Intermediate Certificate. The Bronze Medallion is the standard proficiency award of the Society.

Bronze Medallion

BAR TO THE BRONZE MEDALLION—annual requalification for the Bronze Medallion.

SCHOLAR INSTRUCTOR'S CERTIFICATE—ability to instruct candidates for the Elementary and Intermediate Certificate.

INSTRUCTOR'S CERTIFICATE—ability to instruct candidates for awards up to and including the Bronze Medallion.

BRONZE CROSS & AWARD OF MERIT—these two awards are proof of stamina and watermanship with ability to swim and make a rescue wearing clothes.

Bronze Cross   *Award of Merit*

BARS TO THE BRONZE CROSS AND AWARD OF MERIT—annual requalification.

DISTINCTION AWARD (certificate)—the highest practical award of the Society.

DIPLOMA OF THE SOCIETY (certificate)—a very high standard of practical ability combined with theoretical knowledge.

SAFETY AWARDS

801. These awards are designed to show a standard of competence prior to participating in sports in or on the water and as an introduction for younger children to life saving instruction.

ARTIFICIAL RESPIRATION AWARDS

802. With the exception of the Unigrip Certificate, the above awards require a knowledge of artificial respiration, but the following special artificial respiration awards are available for those unable to take the full course necessary to gain the life saving proficiency awards:

101

(a) **Preliminary Test**—an introductory award.

(b) **Advanced Test**—available to candidates of the age of 16 years and over.

(c) **Advance Test Re-Examination**—periodical requalification.

For (a) and (b) the award is a blue enamel coat badge, pin fitting.

For (c) the award is a certificate.

LIFE GUARD PROFICIENCY TEST

803. The Life Guard Proficiency award is open only to members of the Life Guard Corps. Details of the award will be found in the Life Guard Corps *Handbook*.

REPLACEMENT AWARDS

804. The need for economy, both in money and space in the Headquarters, has necessitated giving up the recording of the names and other details of holders of the Elementary, Intermediate and Unigrip Certificates. In order to deal with those cases in which the original awards are lost in the post, or by other cause, before they are received by successful candidates, the relevant examination forms are kept in the Headquarters for six months from the date of receipt. Once the forms have been destroyed it is possible only in exceptional cases to replace certificates for these awards which are destroyed, lost or mislaid at a later date. All other awards can be replaced on payment of the appropriate fee provided that they can be traced in the Society's records. In case of dispute the Society's records will be taken as final in the absence of other concrete evidence to the contrary.

Requests for replacement awards should state:

(*a*) the award.

(*b*) full name *at the time of examination,*

(*c*) the year and month in which the examination was taken,

(*d*) the name of the club, school or class under which the examination was taken.

Payment of the fee should *not* be made with the initial application, but should await confirmation that the award has been traced, at which time the cost of replacement will be notified. Replacement awards will be of the current design.

GENERAL CONDITIONS FOR EXAMINATIONS

805. Candidates for the Society's life saving awards Membership must be individual members of the Society, or members of a body affiliated to the United Kingdom National Branch or one of its Branches, unless covered by one or more of the following exemptions:

(*a*) candidates for the Elementary Certificate;

(*b*) candidates for the Unigrip Rescue Certificate;

(*c*) candidates for the Artificial Respiration awards;

(*d*) members of Her Majesty's Armed Forces;

(*e*) candidates taking the examination for the Bronze Medallion, the Award of Merit or the Lifeguard Proficiency Test in direct connection with the gaining of an award in the Duke of Edinburgh's Award Scheme.

806. Application for examination should be made Application for examination

(*a*) in the case of candidates within a Branch area, to the Honorary Secretary of the Branch;

103

(*b*) in the case of candidates outside a Branch area, to the local Honorary Representative of the Society, if known, or to the Secretary at the Headquarters of the United Kingdom National Branch.

Application for examination should state the award(s) for which examination is required, whether the appropriate examination forms are held, the number of candidates to be presented, the proposed place of examination and alternative dates and times. A minimum of fourteen days notice should be given. While the Society makes every endeavour to suit the convenience of candidates, it relies entirely on the support of voluntary Examiners and cannot guarantee always to accept the arrangements proposed.

Use of public swimming baths **807.** If the examination is to be conducted in a public swimming bath, responsibility for obtaining the agreement of the Bath Manager rests with the class instructor or, in the case of a single candidate, with the candidate himself.

808. Examinations for the Society's awards may be conducted only by appointed Examiners of the Society, and no such Examiner may examine a candidate with whose instruction in life saving he has been directly concerned, but the National Executive will if necessary modify this rule to meet particular circumstances which arise from time to time in overseas territories forming part of the United Kingdom National Branch provided that written application is made to the Secretary at the Headquarters of the National Branch before the examination is arranged.

809. While it is not the intention to interfere with any arrangement which has been adopted and worked well in the past, the National Executive reserves the right to refuse acceptance of any examination which

104

has not been arranged in accordance with the above rules.

810. Examination fees, which may be altered by the National Executive from time to time, are payable by candidates as follows:

Elementary Certificate		2s. 0d.
Unigrip Rescue Certificate		2s. 6d.
Intermediate Certificate		3s. 0d.
Bronze Medallion		5s. 0d.
First bar		4s. 0d.
Subsequent bars		3s. 0d.
Scholar Instructor's Certificate		3s. 6d.
Instructor's Certificate		5s. 0d.
Bronze Cross		6s. 0d.
First bar		5s. 0d.
Subsequent bars		4s. 0d.
Award of Merit		12s. 6d.
Bars		7s. 6d.
Distinction Award		17s. 6d.
Diploma of the Society	£3	3s. 0d.
Lifeguard Proficiency Test		5s. 0d.
Artificial Respiration award		
Preliminary test		2s. 0d.
Advanced test		5s. 0d.
Advanced test—re-examination		3s. 0d.
Safety Awards		
Preliminary test		3s. 0d.
Advanced test		5s. 0d.

811. Candidates who fail in an examination will forfeit their examination fees. Instructors are advised not to present candidates for examination until they are well up to the standard required.

812. Prior to the commencement of the examination the appropriate examination forms, completed in all required details and with the FULL CHRISTIAN

105

and SURNAMES of all candidates written in BLOCK LETTERS, must be handed to the Examiner. The examination forms are the sole basis for the correct recording and issue of awards. Mistakes in details and illegible writing will result in errors and delay in the receipt of the awards.

Age limit **813.** In examinations for the Bronze Medallion, for which candidates must have attained 14 years of age on the day of examination, unless the birthday falls in the following holiday, Examiners may at their discretion require proof of a candidate's age to be forwarded with the examination form. Such proof should take the form of a statement signed by a responsible person.

Conduct of examinations **814.** Examinations will be conducted in accordance with the current edition of the *Handbook of Instruction*. Tests will normally be carried out in the order set out in the examination conditions, but Examiners have discretion to alter the order of the tests if required by particular circumstances. The primary requirement in the examinations is to prove ability in the Society's methods of life saving and artificial respiration, and a candidate who shows an acceptable standard of life saving proficiency and speed will not be failed solely on imperfection of swimming strokes or diving technique, except in the case of the Diploma. Candidates are not permitted to refer to the *Handbook* or other aids to memory during examination, nor are they allowed to use any artificial aid to swimming.

Safety of candidates **815.** When a class of candidates is under examination the class instructor will be responsible for taking action if a candidate gets into difficulty due to exhaustion or other cause. The decision whether the candidate shall subsequently be permitted to continue the examination will rest with the Examiner after consultation with the instructor. With the above exception the Examiner shall be solely responsible for the conduct of the examination.

816. Candidates will not be required to perform Land drill land drill for the methods of release and rescue, but they will be required to demonstrate methods on land as well as in the water. An Examiner may also require a candidate to demonstrate a method on land if he is not satisfied with the candidate's performance of the method in the water.

817. In schools and other particular cases in which Split examinations it is impossible to conduct the whole examination of a class of candidates in one session, the oral test and the practical demonstration of artificial respiration may be separated from the water work by mutual agreement with the Examiner provided that all candidates shall be ready to take the full examination before commencing any part of it. The period between the two parts of the examination shall not be unduly prolonged, and only in exceptional cases should this period exceed fourteen days.

818. If an examination is split the same Examiner should if possible conduct both sessions.

819. A large class of candidates may be split into sections, each section having a different Examiner.

820. If the minimum depth of water available is Recovery of an object greater than the depth laid down for the recovery of an object, or if the water conditions preclude the sighting of an object on the bottom with reasonable ease, the Examiner should satisfy himself that the candidate can execute a surface dive or swim down, without requiring the actual recovery of an object from the bottom.

821. (*a*) If facilities are not available for tests in Jumping into the water which the candidate is required to jump into the water (e.g. an examination conducted on a beach or at baths where no diving stages are provided), the candidate should be instructed to enter the water in some other way (e.g. wading or jumping into the deep end of the bath). In no circumstances should makeshift arrangements be made to provide a platform.

(*b*) The above alteration to the conditions for examinations applies to examinations up to and including the Bronze Medallion only. No variation to the conditions of awards higher than the Bronze Medallion may be made without the approval of the National Executive.

(*c*) Sub-paragraph 821(*a*) above does not release the Examiner or Instructor from his obligation to the Society under Paragraph 814. Every effort should be made to have the examination conducted in accordance with the full conditions.

Assisting a subject to land

822. The term "assist the subject to land" used in some of the examination conditions means that the subject must be placed in a position of safety. In a swimming bath the subject's hands should be placed on the side of the bath and covered by the candidate's hands to hold them there. In the sea, or in a river with a shallow or shelving bank, the candidate should be assisted to walk from the water.

Clothing

823. In examinations in which other clothes are required to be worn in addition to swimming costume or trunks, such clothing must be of an ordinary everyday character and must be clean. The Examiner at his discretion, or at the request of the Bath Manager when the examination is being held in a public swimming bath, will refuse examination if the clothes worn by the candidate or subject are unsatisfactory in any respect.

Clothing worn overseas

824. The clothing specified in the various examination conditions consists of articles which are normally worn in the United Kingdom. In examinations conducted outside the United Kingdom Examiners have authority to substitute, if necessary, alternative items of clothing appropriate to local conditions provided that the conditions of the tests are not thereby simplified.

825. The subject is not permitted to give the candidate any assistance beyond carrying out instructions given to him verbally by the candidate. Collusion between candidate and subject will entail failure of the candidate and/or the subject if he is also a candidate in the examination.

Collusion between subject and candidate

826. In practical examinations in which the candidate is required to obtain pass marks in each separate test, the candidate shall, if he fails to obtain such pass marks in a particular test, be given the option of carrying on with the examination despite his failure or of terminating the examination without completion of the remaining tests.

Termination of an examination

827. On completion of the examination the Examiner will sign the examination form and indicate the names of candidates who have failed by ruling their names through. The total numbers of passes and failures should be inserted by the Examiner in the appropriate space on the form.

Signature of examination forms

828. Responsibility for ensuring that the completed examination forms are forwarded *without delay* to the Branch or National Headquarters as appropriate (see paragraph 806 above) rests with *the Instructor* of a class, or, in the case of an individual candidate, with *the candidate himself*. Except in those cases in which arrangements exist, or are made, for periodical block payment of fees, the appropriate fees must be sent with the examination forms. Delay in the despatch of awards will occur if this is not done.

Forwarding of forms and fees

829. A minimum period of one year must elapse between the examination for the basic award and the

Bars to awards

taking of the examination for the first bar to that award. For the second and subsequent bars only one bar may be gained in each calendar year and there must be a minimum period of six months between consecutive successful examinations. For example—a candidate who gains the Bronze Cross on 3rd March, 1967, is permitted to take the examination for his first bar to that award at any time after 2nd March, 1968, and does so on 15th May, 1968. Although the minimum period of six months will elapse on 14th November, 1968, he must wait to take the examination for his second bar to the Bronze Cross until 1st January, 1969, because he is not allowed to gain two bars to the same award in the calendar year 1968. This rule does *not* prevent an award holder from taking examinations for bars to two or three separate awards in the same calendar year or within six months of each other.

Approval of National Executive

830. Examination results and the granting of the appropriate proficiency awards are subject to confirmation by the National Executive. Any candidate for a proficiency award being dissatisfied with the conduct (*not* the *result*) of his examination may appeal. Such appeal must in the first instance be sent in writing to the Honorary Secretary of the appropriate Branch or to the Secretary at the National Headquarters.

LIFE SAVING AWARDS
THE ELEMENTARY CERTIFICATE

831. In addition to the general conditions applying to examinations for the Society's awards set out on pages 103 to 110 the following special con-

ditions apply to the examination for the Elementary Certificate:

- (*a*) there is no age limit for candidates;
- (*b*) the examination shall be conducted by one Examiner;
- (*c*) for the water work section of the examination the candidate shall be dressed in swimming costume or trunks as appropriate.

832. The examination will consist of three sections:

- (*a*) an oral test;
- (*b*) a practical demonstration of artificial respiration;
- (*c*) a water work test.

The Oral Test

833. Candidates will be required to answer four questions on the rules for water safety set out in paragraph 20 of the *Handbook* and the principle of Reach-throw-wade-row-swim-tow described in paragraph 31.

Artificial Respiration

834. Candidates will be required to demonstrate the Expired Air (mouth-to-nose or mouth-to-mouth) or the Silvester-Brosch method of artificial respiration, |

the choice of method being made by the candidate. The candidate will be required to demonstrate the action to be taken if the patient vomits.

Water Work

835. (*a*) Enter the water and tread water for 1 minute, keeping the face above the surface all the time.

(*b*) Recover an object (5 to 10 lb) from the bottom in 5 feet of water and bring it to land. The approach swim must be commenced from a point at least 5 yards from the position of the object.

(*c*) Swim 50 yards by any stroke other than the life saving back kick, and 25 yards on the back—legs only, showing ability to change direction left and right; during the swim on the back the arms must be folded, or crossed on the chest or abdomen; the full distance of 75 yards must be done without pause as one continuous swim.

(*d*) Swim 10 yards head-up and approach the subject from behind; tow the subject by a head carry (chosen by the candidate) for a distance of 10 yards.

(*e*) Swim 10 yards head-up to the subject; give the subject the necessary verbal instructions and then rescue him over a distance of 10 yards using a tired swimmer method.

THE INTERMEDIATE CERTIFICATE

836. In addition to the general conditions applying to examinations for the Society's awards set out on pages 103 to 110 the following special conditions apply to the examination for the Intermediate Certificate:

(*a*) there is no age limit for candidates taking the examination;

(*b*) the examination shall be conducted by one Examiner;

(*c*) for the water work section of the examination the candidate shall be dressed in swimming costume or trunks as appropriate;

(*d*) an unsuccessful candidate for the Bronze Medallion may at the discretion of the Examiner be recommended for the award of the Intermediate Certificate without payment of a further fee;

(*e*) a successful candidate for the Bronze Medallion shall, if he so wishes, also be awarded the Intermediate Certificate without further examination upon payment of the appropriate fee.

837. The examination will consist of three sections:

(*a*) an oral test;

(*b*) a practical demonstration of artificial respiration;

(*c*) a water work test.

The Oral Test

838. Candidates will be required to answer a minimum of four questions on the general principles of saving life from drowning and artificial respiration as set out in the *Handbook*. They will be required to show an understanding of the simple functions of the heart, lungs and blood stream, and how these combine together to maintain the supply of oxygen to the brain. Candidates will not be required to memorise medical names and terms. (See paragraphs 712 to 723.)

Artificial Respiration (Practical)

839. Candidates will be required to perform *one* of the following tests as chosen by them:

(a) Demonstrate for a continuous period of 2 minutes the Expired Air (mouth-to-nose or mouth-to-mouth) method of artificial respiration; demonstrate the action to be taken if the patient vomits.

(b) Demonstrate for a continuous period of 2 minutes the Silvester-Brosch method of artificial respiration; demonstrate the action to be taken if the patient vomits.

Water Work

840. (a) Demonstrate on land two methods of release; one clutch will be ordered by the Examiner, the other may be chosen by the candidate (see paragraph 301). Demonstrate the same two methods of release in the water; after breaking the clutch the candidate will turn the subject to the towing position to complete the movement.

(b) Jump into the water from a height of 1 to 3 feet, making the shallowest entry possible, as for a muddy bottom; swim 20 yards, making a head-up approach to the subject who will be positioned with his back to the candidate; support the subject from behind in the same spot for 2 minutes without any assistance from him.

(c) Tow the subject 15 yards by a head carry; the method to be used will be ordered by the Examiner. Assist the subject to land (see paragraph 822).

(d) Enter the water by any method. Make a head-up approach over a distance of 10 yards, recover an object (5 to 10 lb) from the bottom in 6 feet of water (or the nearest depth available below that figure, but not less than 5 feet), and bring it to land. If the candidate fails at his first attempt, he must be successful in two out of the next three attempts.

(e) Make a shallow dive entry, or jump, into the water and a head-up approach to the subject over a distance of 50 yards. Approach the subject from the rear and tow him 15 yards by a body carry ordered by the Examiner.

(f) Swim 50 yards within 70 seconds by any stroke to the subject; give him verbal instructions what to do and then rescue him over a distance of 20 yards using a tired swimmer method; assist the subject from the water.

841. In addition to the general conditions applying to all examinations for the Society's awards set out on pages 103 to 110 the following special conditions apply to the examination for the Unigrip Certificate:

(a) There is no age limit for candidates taking the examination;

(b) the examination shall be conducted by one Examiner;

(c) candidates shall be dressed in swimming costume or trunks as appropriate.

842. Candidates will be required to perform the following test in one continuous swim:

(a) carry the subject 20 yards by the "Unigrip" method;

(b) carry the subject 20 yards by the "Unigrip" method demonstrating the method of restraint;

(c) carry the subject 20 yards demonstrating the supplementary method of restraint.

THE BRONZE MEDALLION

843. In addition to the general conditions applying to examinations for the Society's awards set out on pages 103 to 110 the following special conditions apply to the examination for the Bronze Medallion:

(*a*) a candidate shall be 14 years of age or over on the day of examination, candidates will be permitted to take the test while under 14 years of age provided that their 14th birthday falls between the time of the termly examination and the start of the next term and that the award is withheld until the 14th birthday;

(*b*) the examination shall be conducted by one Examiner;

(*c*) for the water work section of the examination the candidate shall be dressed in swimming costume or trunks as appropriate;

(*d*) a candidate who fails in the examination for the Bronze Medallion may be recommended by the Examiner at his discretion for the award of the Intermediate Certificate in lieu without payment of a further fee, but no part of the fee already paid shall be returned; the examination form must be completed by the Examiner accordingly;

(*e*) a successful candidate for the Bronze Medallion shall, if he so wishes, also be awarded the Intermediate Certificate without further examination upon payment of the appropriate fee. The names of candidates wishing to avail themselves of this option must be inserted in the appropriate

column of the examination form at the end of the
examination, and before its signature by the
Examiner. The additional fees payable must be
included in the fees forwarded with the examination form.

Note: The Standard Pocket Certificate for members
of H.M. Forces has been abandoned because of lack
of demand for it.

844. The examination will consist of three sections:

(*a*) an oral test;

(*b*) a practical demonstration of artificial respiration;

(*c*) a water work test.

The Oral Test

845. Candidates will be required to answer a minimum of six questions on the general principles of
saving life from drowning as set out in the *Handbook*.
They will be required to show a knowledge of the
simple functions of the heart, lungs and blood stream,
and how these combine together to maintain the supply
of oxygen to the brain. Candidates will not be required to memorise medical names and terms. (See
paragraphs 712 to 723.) The test will include simple
questions on the principle of artificial respiration, and
questions on the adaptation of the various methods
when used on frail or injured patients, children and
infants, and the treatment of patients after normal
breathing has been restored. (From 1st September,
1967, questions on External Cardiac Compression
will be included in this test.)

Artificial Respiration (Practical)

846. Candidates will be required to perform the
following tests:

118

(a) Demonstrate, using a manikin or mask, the Expired Air mouth-to-nose method, and the mouth-to-mouth method using the cheek or fingers to seal the patient's nostrils; demonstrate the action to be taken in case of vomiting by the patient; demonstrate the action to be taken if air enters the patient's stomach;

If no manikin or mask is available the first section of the above test will be:

Demonstrate the correct positioning of the head on a live subject, and then carry out the movements of breathing for the mouth-to-nose and mouth-to-mouth methods as laid down in the training drill.

(b) Demonstrate the Silvester-Brosch method for a continuous period of at least 2 minutes; demonstrate the action to be taken if the patient vomits.

Water Work

847. (a) Demonstrate on land one method of release from a clutch selected by the Examiner (see paragraph 301) and one method of rescue as directed by the Examiner. Demonstrate the same method of release in the water, and tow the subject for 10 yards by the same method of rescue. (If necessary, there must be a "break" between the release and the tow.) Assist the subject to land (see paragraph 822).

(b) Carry out the following test in one continuous sequence: enter the water feet-first from a height of 5 to 8 feet making the shallowest possible entry and swim 200 yards within 6 minutes; during the last 20 yards of this swim make a head-up approach to the subject, submerge to pass to one side or the other (*not* underneath) the subject and then surface and approach the subject from behind; support the subject for 30 seconds, then tow him for 20 yards using any head carry method. Change direction as ordered by the Examiner during the tow. Assist the subject to land.

(c) Tread water continuously for 2 minutes.

(d) Make a shallow dive entry, swim 50 yards and approach the subject head up during the last 10 yards. Release from the clutch used by the subject. The clutch to be used by the subject (which should differ from that used in (a) above) will be ordered by the Examiner and will not be revealed to the candidate. Tow the subject for 20 yards by the Unigrip method. The subject will struggle for at least five yards of the tow, as directed by the Examiner, and the candidate will take the appropriate action.

(e) From the surface of the water recover from the bottom in a depth of 7 feet (or the nearest depth of water available below that figure, but not less than 5 feet) an object (5 to 10 lb) and bring it to land. If the candidate fails at his first attempt, the test must be repeated three times and must be successfully completed on each occasion.

Note for Examiners

848. If the subject is also a candidate in the examination, the time required for the examination will be shortened if the subject is put in his appropriate position in the water for the test in paragraph 847(b) and then carries out the test in paragraph 847(c) while waiting for the candidate to complete his 200 yards swim. The candidate would similarly do his test 847(c) when acting as the subject for test 847(b).

THE SCHOLAR-INSTRUCTOR'S CERTIFICATE

849. In addition to the general conditions applying to examinations for the Society's awards set out on pages 103 to 110 the following special conditions apply to the examination for the Scholar-Instructor's Certificate:

(a) a candidate must be attending as a full-time pupil at an educational establishment; he must hold the Bronze Medallion;

(b) the examination shall be conducted by one Examiner.

850. The candidate shall present for examination a class of a minimum of four and a maximum of eight candidates for the Intermediate Certificate, none of whom shall have previously taken the examination for that award. The training of this class must have been the unaided work of the candidate-Scholar-Instructor who will be required to sign a statement to that effect on his examination form. If the class consists of four candidates, three must successfully pass the examination. If the number in the class is greater than four, the number of successful candidates must be:

Number in class	Number of successful candidates
5	4
6	4
7	5
8	6

851. In addition to the above requirement, the candidate must prove his ability as an instructor in the following tests:

5

(*a*) instruct the class on land in a method of release or rescue, selected by the Examiner, correcting mistakes as necessary;

(*b*) instruct the class on a point concerning the blood circulation, respiration or resuscitation, selected by the Examiner;

(*c*) answer questions by the Examiner on the general principles of saving life from drowning and the treatment of the apparently drowned as set out in the *Handbook* (from 1st September, 1967, questions on External Cardiac Compression will be included);

(*d*) give a demonstration in the water of two of the following items, selected by the Examiner—a method of release or rescue, surface dive, breast or other head-up stroke, a back stroke. Explain the common faults in the movements demonstrated and describe how they are corrected.

THE INSTRUCTOR'S CERTIFICATE

852. In addition to the general conditions applying to examinations for the Society's awards set out on pages 103 to 110 the following special conditions apply to the examination for the Instructor's Certificate;

- (*a*) a candidate must hold the Bronze Medallion and be 16 years of age or over on the day of examintion;

- (*b*) the examination shall be conducted by one Examiner.

853. The candidate shall present for examination a class of a minimum of four and a maximum of eight candidates for the Bronze Medallion, none of whom shall have previously taken the examination for that award. The training of this class must have been the unaided work of the candidate Instructor who will be required to sign a statement to that effect on his examination form. If the class consists of four candidates, three must successfully pass the examination. If the number in the class is greater than four, the number of successful candidates must be:

Number in class	Number of successful candidates
5	4
6	4
7	5
8	6

854. In addition to the above requirement the candidate must prove his ability as an instructor in the following tests:

(a) instruct the class on land in one method of release and one method of rescue, selected by the Examiner, correcting mistakes as necessary;

(b) instruct the class on a point, selected by the Examiner, concerning the functions of the heart or lungs, blood circulation, respiration or resuscitation (External Cardiac Compression will be included from 1st September, 1967);

(c) answer questions by the Examiner on the general principles of saving life from drowning and the treatment of the apparently drowned as set out in the *Handbook* (from 1st September, 1967, questions on External Cardiac Compression will be included);

(d) give a demonstration of External Cardiac Compression (from 1st September, 1967);

(e) give a demonstration in the water of three of the following items, selected by the Examiner—a method of release or rescue, surface dive, feet-first entry from a height of 5 to 8 feet, breast or other head-up stroke, a back stroke. Explain the common faults in the movements demonstrated and describe how they are corrected.

THE BRONZE CROSS

855. In addition to the general conditions applying to all examinations for the Society's awards set out on pages 103 to 110 the following special conditions apply to the examination for the Bronze Cross:

(a) a candidate for the Bronze Cross must have previously gained the Bronze Medallion of the Society and in case of doubt may be required to produce proof of such qualification; in the absence of other concrete evidence the Society's records shall be final;

(b) the examination shall be conducted by one Examiner, Grade 1;

(c) a maximum of 10 marks is allotted to each test, or separately numbered part of a test. Pass marks will be an average marking for all tests of not less than 6 marks, and not less than 5 marks in any individual test;

(d) candidates shall be dressed as follows at the commencement of the examination:

>*Ladies*—swimming costume, blouse and skirt which must be properly fastened; slacks are a permissable alternative to a skirt.

>*Men*—swimming costume or trunks, singlet and cloth, flannel or drill trousers secured by belt or braces.

>Subjects shall be dressed in swimming costume or trunks as appropriate.

Clothing shall be of an ordinary everyday character and must be clean. The Examiner at his discretion, or at the request of the Bath Manager when the examination is being held in a swimming bath, will refuse examination to a candidate whose clothes are unsatisfactory in any respect.

Warning Note. The attention of candidates is drawn to the warning note in paragraph 857 which, although not applying to the Bronze Cross examination, emphasises the need to ensure that the neck opening of the singlet worn is sufficiently large to allow its removal over the head in the water without risk. Singlets in which the neck opening has been artificially enlarged by cutting or tearing will *not* be accepted by the Examiner.

856. The examination will consist of the following tests:

(a) *Release and towing methods*

Demonstrate on land, and then in the water, three methods of release, the clutch to be used in each case being ordered by the Examiner.

On land, the subject and rescuer will take up position and the subject will apply the clutch. On the order "Break" the candidate will release the clutch, turn the subject, if necessary, and apply an appropriate towing hold. The same procedure will be used in the water, the subject being towed for 10 yards on each occasion.

(b) *A long distance swim followed by a tow*

This is a test of the candidate's stamina and is a special examination condition. In practice a rescuer would normally remove as much clothing as possible before embarking on a swim of this distance. Enter the water, dressed as above, and swim

(i) 50 yards on the back using *no* arm movement;

126

(ii) 90 yards by any stroke of the candidate's choice;

(iii) 10 yards approach to the subject (who will be positioned in the right place by the Examiner) using the breast-stroke or other head-up stroke of the candidate's choice. Tow the subject 40 yards by a method ordered by the Examiner. Circling turns should be used if conditions make turns necessary during the tow.

The above test must be carried out in one continuous movement without pause.

(c) **Undressing in the water**

In deep water remove all clothing except swimming costume or trunks within 30 seconds.

(d) *Recovery of an object*

Recover *twice* an object weighing 5 to 10 lb from a depth of 7 feet (or the nearest depth available, but not less than 6 feet). The candidate will, if necessary, be allowed a total of three attempts to recover the object of which two must be successful.

(e) *Timed swim followed by a tow*

Swim 200 yards within 6 minutes using any strokes of the candidate's choice during the first 190 yards; in the final 10-yards approach to the subject a head-up stroke is to be used. Tow the subject 20 yards using the method ordered by the Examiner; this method will differ from that used in test (b) above. Assist the subject to land (see paragraph 822).

Rest Periods

The candidate will be allowed a rest of one minute between each of the tests (a) to (e) above.

THE AWARD OF MERIT

857. In addition to the general conditions applying to all examinations for the Society's awards set out on pages 103 to 110 the following special conditions apply to the examination for the Award of Merit:

(*a*) a candidate for the Award of Merit must have previously gained the Bronze Medallion of the Society and in case of doubt may be required to produce proof of such qualification; in the absence of other concrete evidence the Society's records shall be final;

(*b*) the examination shall be conducted by one Examiner, Grade 1;

(*c*) a maximum of 10 marks is allotted to each test, or separately numbered part of a test. Pass marks will be an average marking for all tests of not less than 6 marks, and not less than 5 marks in any individual test.

(*d*) candidates and subjects shall be dressed as follows at the commencement of the examination:

> *Ladies*—swimming costume, stockings held up by suspenders, skirt which must be properly fastened, blouse and cardigan or jumper, one of which must have long sleeves; slacks and socks are a permissible alternative to skirt and stockings.

> *Men*—swimming costume or trunks, shirt and cardigan or pullover, one of which must have long sleeves, cloth, flannel or drill trousers, belt or braces, socks which must be securely fastened.

Clothing shall be of an ordinary everyday character and must be clean. The Examiner at his discretion, or at the request of the Bath Manager when the examination is being held in a swimming bath, will refuse examination if the clothes of the candidate or his subject are unsatisfactory in any respect.

Warning Note. Because of the increasing use of man-made fibres in the material used for clothing the requirement that shirts and similar garments should be removed over the head has been deleted. Buttons on wet garments made of nylon type fabrics often become difficult to undo; if in these circumstances an attempt is made to remove the garment over the head with a neck opening which is too small, it is apt to become wrapped round the wearer's head and to obstruct his breathing. If the shirt or other garment worn cannot be completely unbuttoned down the front, and must therefore be removed over the head, it should be made of some natural fibre material, such as cotton.

858. The examination will consist of two sections:

(*a*) a practical and oral test of resuscitation;

(*b*) a water work test.

Resuscitation

859. (*a*) Demonstrate the following methods of resuscitation, each demonstration being for a minimum period of 2 minutes:

(i) Expired Air method, followed by action to deal with vomiting by the patient,

(ii) Silvester-Brosch method, followed by action to deal with vomiting by the patient,

(iii) External Cardiac Compression (from 1st September, 1967).

(*b*) Describe, and if necessary amplify by answering questions, the after-care of a revived patient.

860. (*a*) *A long distance swim in clothes followed by release and tow*

This is a test of the candidate's stamina and is a special examination condition. In practice a rescuer would normally remove as much clothing as possible before embarking on a swim of this distance.

Enter the water dressed as above and swim 200 yards, the final 20-yards approach to the subject being made using a head-up stroke. During this swim the candidate may use any stroke of his choice excluding back strokes, but the stroke used during the second 90 yards must differ from that used during the first 90 yards. Make the head-up approach to the subject who will have been positioned in the right place by the Examiner.

Apply the appropriate release to break the clutch which will be ordered by the Examiner and not previously revealed to the candidate, tow the subject 40 yards by the method ordered by the Examiner, and assist the subject to land. The method of towing will be made known to the candidate before the commencement of the test.

The time allowed for the completion of this test is **10 minutes.**

(*b*) *Recovery of an object from the bottom*

Wearing clothes as in the previous test recover an object weighing 5 to 10 lb from a depth of 7 feet (or the nearest depth available but not less than 6 feet),

(i) by surface dive or swimming down head-first,

(ii) by submerging feet-first.

In each of the above tests, if the candidate fails at his first attempt, two of the next three attempts must be successful.

(c) *Medium distance swim followed by tow*

Dressed as for the previous test, enter the water from a height of 3 feet in any manner, making the shallowest entry possible as for unknown water. Swim 100 yards and approach the subject using appropriate action (e.g. underwater approach) to avoid being clutched. Approach the subject from behind and tow him for 20 yards by the method ordered by the Examiner; the method will differ from that used in test (a) above. Assist the subject to land.

The time allowed for completion of this test is **8 minutes.**

Note for Examiners

If the subjects in the above tests are also candidates, *all* candidates should complete tests (a), (b) and (c), and then (d), before continuing with the remainder of the examination.

(d) *Undressing in the water*

In deep water remove all clothing except swimming trunks or costume within 25 seconds.

(Subjects who are not candidates remove clothing other than swimming trunks or costume.)

(e) *A one-handed tow*

Tow the subject for 50 yards by any one-handed method not previously used in the examination, the choice of method resting with the candidate.

(f) *Entry from a height followed by rescue, landing and artificial respiration*

Enter the water by a jump or dive from a height of 8 to 10 feet towards the subject in deep water. Tow the subject, now assumed to be unconscious, to the nearest point of land by any method. Land the subject unaided, prepare him for artificial respiration and apply *three* breathing cycles using either the Expired Air or the Silvester-Brosch method. The choice of method resting with the candidate.

Note for Examiners

Conditions in some swimming baths or unacceptable risk of injury to the subject may make it undesirable to carry out the actual landing. In these circumstances the candidate should be required to demonstrate the method without making the actual landing, or, if necessary to describe how it would be done.

BARS TO THE BRONZE MEDALLION, BRONZE CROSS AND AWARD OF MERIT

861. Paragraphs 28 and 923 emphasise the need for continued practise in life saving. In order to encourage holders of the Society's life saving proficiency awards to re-qualify from time to time bars to the Bronze Medallion, Bronze Cross and the Award of Merit are available under the conditions set out in paragraph 829. The award of the first bar will be two bars and a length of ribbon in the Society's colours, the upper bar bearing the letters R.L.S.S. and the lower bar "1st". For the Bronze Medallion both bars will be in bronze, for the Bronze Cross the upper bar will be in bronze and the lower bar in bronze and yellow enamel and for the Award of Merit both bars will be in gilt and blue enamel. Subsequent bars will be similar to the appropriate lower bar but bearing the number of the bar gained, i.e., "2nd", "3rd", etc.

DISTINCTION AWARD

862. In addition to the general conditions applying to all examinations set out on pages 103 to 110, the following special conditions apply to the examination for the Distinction Award:

(*a*) a candidate for the Distinction Award must be a holder of the Award of Merit, and in case of doubt may be required to produce proof of such qualification; in the absence of other concrete evidence the Society's records shall be final;

(*b*) the examination shall be conducted by two Grade 1 Examiners;

(*c*) no deviation from the examination conditions (other than that allowed by paragraph 824 of the general conditions) will be permitted on account of the lack of a facility; candidates must be prepared to take the examination in a swimming bath or other place in which all the required facilities are available;

(*d*) a maximum of 10 marks is allotted to each test, or separately numbered part of a test; pass marks will be an average marking for all tests of not less than 6 marks, and not less than 5 marks in any individual test;

(*e*) candidates and subjects shall be dressed as follows at the commencement of the examination:

> *Ladies*—swimming costume, stockings held up by suspenders, skirt which must be properly fastened, blouse and cardigan or jumper, one of which must have long sleeves; slacks and socks are a permissible alternative to skirt and stockings;

Men—swimming costume or trunks, shirt and cardigan or pullover, one of which must have long sleeves, cloth, flannel or drill trousers, belt or braces, and socks which must be securely fastened;

Clothing shall be of an ordinary everyday character and must be clean. The Examiner at his discretion, or at the request of the Bath Manager when the examination is being held in a swimming bath, will refuse examination if the clothes of the candidate or his subject are unsatisfactory in any respect.

Warning Note: Because of the increasing use of man-made fibres in the material used for clothing the requirement that shirts and similar garments should be removed over the head has been deleted. Buttons on wet garments made of nylon type fabrics often become difficult to undo; if in these circumstances an attempt is made to remove the garment over the head with a neck opening which is too small, it is apt to become wrapped round the wearer's head and to obstruct his breathing. If the shirt or other garment worn cannot be completely unbuttoned down the front, and must therefore be removed over the head, it should be made of some natural fibre material, such as cotton.

(*f*) an optional rest of one minute will be allowed between each test in the water.

863. The examination will consist of two sections:

(*a*) a practical and oral test of resuscitation;

(*b*) a water work test.

Resuscitation

864. (*a*) Demonstrate the following methods of resuscitation, each demonstration being for a minimum period of 2 minutes:

    (i) Expired Air method, followed by action to deal with vomiting by the patient;

    (ii) Silvester-Brosch method, followed by action to deal with vomiting by the patient;

    (iii) External Cardiac Compression (from 1st September, 1967).

(*b*) Describe, and if necessary amplify by answering questions, the after-care of a revived patient.

Water Work

865. (*a*) Jump into the water, dressed as above, and swim 200 yards by any front stroke within **5 minutes.** Recover an object (minimum weight 7 lb) from a minimum depth of 7 feet. The subject, clothed as above, will be positioned by the Examiner while the candidate is performing the above part of the test. On a signal from the Examiner, drop the object and tow the subject (assumed to be unconscious) by a one-handed method over a distance of not less than 20 yards. Make a shallow water landing and perform artificial respiration on the subject for 3 cycles.

(*b*) Enter deep water and remove all clothes except swimming costume or trunks. Swim 300 yards to the subject (clothed) and tow him 50 yards by any method of the candidate's choice. Land the subject at any convenient point and apply artificial respiration for 3 cycles.

The time allowed from entry into the water to arrival at the landing point is 7½ **minutes** for men and 8½ **minutes** for women.

(*c*) Enter the water from a height of 6 to 8 feet, dressed in swimming trunks or costume, as close as is safe to two subjects (dressed in swimming trunks or costume) who represent two weak or exhausted swimmers locked together as ordered by the Examiner. Separate and reassure the subjects, make a **double** carry rescue over a distance of 20 yards and assist the subjects to land.

(*d*) Demonstrate in the water release from four different clutches detailed by the Examiner, and not previously revealed to the candidate. After the fourth release, tow the subject demonstrating four different methods of towing detailed by the Examiner, for at least 20 yards in each case. After the last tow demonstrate a deep-water landing.

866. In addition to the general conditions applying to all examinations for the Society's awards set out on pages 103 to 110, the following special conditions apply to the examination for the Diploma of the Society:

(*a*) a candidate for the Diploma must be 17 years of age or over on the date on which the practical test is taken, and must hold the Award of Merit. In case of doubt the candidate may be required to provide proof of these qualifications; in the case of the latter qualification the Society's records shall be final in the absence of other concrete evidence;

(*b*) Application for examination must be made in writing to the Honorary Secretary of the Branch, if the candidate resides in a Branch area, or to the Secretary at the Headquarters of the National Branch. The application must give the full name and address of the candidate and the date and place of examination for the Award of Merit, and must be accompanied by the examination fee of three guineas.

(*c*) The examination will consist of a practical test and a written examination. The practical test, which will be conducted by two Grade 1 Examiners appointed in accordance with instructions issued from time to time by the National Executive, may be taken in sea or fresh water, and must be taken not less than twenty-eight days before the written examination which will be held on a Saturday in May and October of each year, (very exceptionally examinations may be held at other times by arrangements with Headquarters in the case of organised courses). The examination form for the practical test must be forwarded to the Branch or to the National Headquarters, as appropriate, immediately on completion of the practical examination. The written examination must be taken within eight months of the date of the practical test. Only in exceptional cases, such as illness, will candidates be permitted to postpone their written examination until the next occasion. In such cases the candidate should immediately inform the Branch or the National Headquarters, as appropriate;

(*d*) Candidates who obtain not less than 60 per cent. of the maximum marks in the practical test and in the written examination, and not less than 50 per cent. in each separate section of the practical test and for each question in the written examination, will be awarded the Diploma of the Society. Candidates who obtain not less than 75 per cent. of the marks for each separate section of the practical test, and not less than 80 per cent. for each question in the written examination will be awarded the Diploma with Honours.

(*e*) A candidate failing in any part of the examination will forfeit the fee paid.

(*f*) A candidate who passes the practical test and fails in the written examination shall have the option of sitting for the next written examination, without again taking the practical test, on payment of a further fee of two guineas and provided that notice of his intention to do so is given not less than twenty-eight days before the date of the next written examination.

Practical Test

867. No deviation from the following conditions (other than that allowed by paragraph 824 of the general conditions) will be permitted on account of the lack of a facility; candidates must be prepared to take the examination in a swimming bath or other places in which all the required facilities are available.

At the commencement of the examination candidates shall be dressed as follows:

Ladies—swimming costume, stockings held up by suspenders, skirt which must be properly fastened, blouse and cardigan or jumper, one of which must have long sleeves, plimsolls. Slacks and socks are a permissible alternative to skirt and stockings.

Men—swimming costume or trunks, shirt and cardigan or pullover, one of which must have long sleeves, cloth, flannel or drill trousers, belt or braces, socks which must be securely fastened, plimsolls.

Subjects will be dressed as above throughout the examination.

Clothing shall be of an ordinary everyday character and must be clean. The Examiner at his discretion, or at the request of the Bath Manager when the examination is being held in a swimming bath, will refuse examination if the clothes of the candidate or his subject are unsatisfactory in any respect.

Warning Note. Because of the increasing use of man-made fibres in the material used for clothing the requirement that shirts and similar garments should be removed over the head has been deleted. Buttons on wet garments made of nylon type fabrics often become difficult to undo; if in these circumstances an attempt is made to remove the garment over the head with a neck opening which is too small, it is apt to become wrapped round the wearer's head and to obstruct his breathing. If the shirt or other garment worn cannot be completely unbuttoned down the front, and must therefore be removed over the head, it should be made of some natural fibre material, such as cotton.

868. The practical test will consist of the following sections taken in the order named:

(a) Apply resuscitation, for a period of 2 minutes in each case, to victims of two of the following types of accident; describe all other steps to be taken from the moment of finding the victims: (i) Drowning, (ii) Strangulation, (iii) Electric shock, (iv) Carbon monoxide poisoning. The types of accident and the methods of artificial respiration to be applied will be detailed by the Examiner. (External Cardiac Compression will be included from 1st September, 1967.)

(b) Make a feet-first entry from a minimum height of 8 feet. Swim 200 yards, clothed as above, and recover an object (minimum weight 7 lb) from a depth of 8 to 10 feet. Tread water and exchange the object for an adult subject dressed as above and having a minimum weight of 9 stone. Tread water and support the subject for 2 minutes. **(The time allowed for this test is 7 minutes.)** (*Optional rest* of 2 minutes.)

(c) In deep water, remove all clothing (except swimming costume or trunks) in any order and in any manner. Swim 200 yards to the subject, effect a release, and tow the subject for a distance of 200 yards using at least two different methods of rescue. Remove the subject from the water without assistance and apply artificial respiration for 1 minute. **(The time allowed for this test is 12 minutes.)**

The subject will be briefed by the Examiner concerning the clutch to be used and his subsequent behaviour while being rescued; this information will not be revealed to the candidate who must use methods of release and rescue suitable to the subject's actions. The method of artificial respiration to be used will be detailed by the Examiner. (*Optional rest* of 2 minutes.)

(*d*) Make two consecutive tows, each of 100 yards; the towing methods to be used will be detailed by the Examiner and will differ from the methods already used in the examination. **(The time allowed for this test is 7 minutes.)**

(*e*) Scull a distance of 30 feet head-first, make a turn and scull back to the starting point.

(*f*) Demonstrate three of the following swimming strokes, each demonstration being over a distance of 100 yards:
(i) Breast-stroke, (ii) Front-crawl, (iii) Back-crawl, (iv) Life-saving back-stroke without use of arms, (v) Side-stroke.

(*g*) Demonstrate a release from a back stranglehold.

(*h*) Diving. Demonstrate:
(i) a shallow-entry dive from a low take-off (not above 3 feet or 1 metre);
(ii) a plain header or jump from a height of 8 to 11 feet.

The Written Examination

869. The examination paper will consist of **six** questions based on the following syllabus:

(*a*) The importance of physical exercise on the growth and development of the body, with special reference to the effect of swimming.
The importance and advantages of swimming to the individual and to the community.

(b) The fundamental physiology concerning the structure and functions of the lungs, the circulation of the blood and muscle nutrition.

(c) The effects of, and recuperation from, moderate and excessive exercise. The treatment of cramp.

(d) The causes of, and the steps to be taken to remedy, asphyxia (particularly electric shock, strangulation, carbon monoxide poisoning and drowning); shock, its action and treatment.

(e) Modern trends of thought in relation to Life Saving and Resuscitation.

870. A list of reference books recommended for study and notes for the guidance of intending candidates can be obtained on application to the Honorary Branch Secretaries or to the National Headquarters.

871. The time and place of the examination, and the appointment of invigilators will be arranged by the Branch or National Headquarters as appropriate. The examination paper will be supplied from the National Headquarters in a sealed envelope which will be opened by the invigilator in the presence of the candidate(s) at the commencement of the examination.

872. Candidates will be required to answer *five* of the six questions in the paper, and not more than five. The time allowed for the examination will be three hours. Candidates may not refer to any books, papers or other aids to memory during the examination.

873. A candidate who writes his answers to the paper in a language other than English will be responsible for bearing the cost of subsequent translation which will be arranged by the authority conducting the candidate's examination (National Headquarters, Branch or Honorary Representative). The candidate will not be permitted to arrange for the translation of his answers. Examination papers will be set only in the English language.

SAFETY AWARDS

874. In addition to the general conditions applying to examinations for the Society's awards set out on pages 103 to 110 the following special conditions apply to the Safety Awards:

(*a*) there is no age limit for candidates;

(*b*) for the water work sections of the examinations the candidates shall be dressed as follows:

Ladies and girls—dress, or blouse and slacks, or pyjamas, to be worn over swimming costume.

Men and boys—trousers and shirt, or pyjamas, to be worn over swimming trunks.

875.   THE PRELIMINARY TEST

Artificial Respiration

876. Demonstrate knowledge of a method of artificial respiration or present an artificial respiration certificate.

Water Work

877. Carry out the following tests in one continuous sequence:

(*a*) Enter the water feet first and swim 50 yards.

(*b*) Tread water for 1 minute.

(*c*) In deep water remove all clothing except swimming costume or trunks.

144

(d) Surface dive in a depth of not less than 4 feet and use feet to push off the bottom.

(e) Swim 200 yards by any stroke.

(f) Scull head or feet first for 30 feet.

878.   THE ADVANCED TEST

Artificial Respiration

879. Demonstrate either Expired Air or Silvester-Brosch methods of artificial respiration for at least 1 minute or present an artificial respiration certificate.

Water Work

880. Carry out the following tests in one continuous sequence:

(a) Enter the water feet first from a height of 5 to 10 feet.

(b) Swim 100 yards in not more than 4 minutes.

(c) Tread water for 3 minutes; 1 minute with the legs only, 2 minutes with the arms only.

(d) Recover an object weighing 5 to 10 lb from a depth of 6 feet (or nearest depth available but not less than 5 feet) and land object.

(e) In deep water remove all clothing except swimming costume or trunks in less than 20 seconds.

(f) Swim 200 yards on the back without use of arms or artificial aids.

(g) Swim 200 yards freestyle, other than backstroke without arms.

(h) Scull head and feet first each for 30 feet.

(i) Leave deep water without use of steps or assistance.

145

PART NINE

ADMINISTRATION

The Appointment and Duties of Honorary Representatives

900. Honorary Representatives are appointed by the National Executive to supervise the work of the National Branch in appropriate towns and districts in the Non-Branch areas. They correspond direct with the National Headquarters, and the following notes are set out for their guidance. For brevity the notes refer only to the masculine gender.

901. Honorary Representatives in the Branch areas are appointed by the Branch Executive Committees whose representatives they are, and with whom they correspond.

902. It is generally desirable that an Honorary Representative should already be an experienced Examiner, but this is not an obligatory requirement for appointment.

Purpose

903. The twofold purpose of the Honorary Representative is to act as the local representative of the Society in all matters connected with its work, keeping the National Executive informed of such matters, and to further the work by introducing it into schools, colleges, clubs and other appropriate organisations in which life saving and artificial respiration are not being taught.

Area of responsibility

904. The area covered by an Honorary Representative depends largely on the travel facilities available and the amount of time which he can devote to the work. It is agreed on appointment, but the National Executive will always welcome and consider a proposal to widen the area if subsequent changes make this possible. The lack of detailed definition of the areas covered by Honorary Representatives makes it important that each should keep in touch with neighbouring Representatives to avoid overlapping and duplication.

905. The arrangement of examinations is an Arrangement of examinations important aspect of the Honorary Representative's work. Applications for examinations in his area received direct at Headquarters are forwarded to him for arrangement unless time does not permit. In this case the arrangements are made by Headquarters and he is informed of them. The Honorary Representative is expected to keep a list of the Examiners resident in his area, and to share the examinations between them so that all are given an opportunity to render the voluntary service which they offer to the Society by becoming Examiners. It is hoped that Honorary Representatives will themselves conduct a proportion of the examinations and so ensure that the necessary high standard of instruction and performance is being maintained in their areas.

906. The Honorary Representative is expected to arbitrate on any point of disagreement arising in his area from differing interpretations of the examination conditions. When this cannot properly be done locally, the matter should be referred to the Headquarters for direction or decision by the National Executive.

907. The success of the Society's work depends very Appointment of new examiners largely on having an adequate pool of Examiners. Honorary Representatives can give great help in this respect by encouraging suitable award holders and others to become Examiners. Such persons must be suitable in all respects to represent the Society in this important position and must be likely to maintain the high standard of performance required from candidates for the proficiency awards, bearing in mind that a candidate who gains such an award when below standard is more likely to be a danger to himself than a help to another in difficulty. The method of applying for appointment as an Examiner is described in paragraphs 914 to 918.

Headquarters panel of examiners

908. A complete list of Examiners in the Non-Branch areas is maintained at Headquarters and it is helpful in keeping this list up-to-date if Honorary Representatives inform Headquarters of changes in their local lists as and when they occur. Similarly Headquarters informs Honorary Representatives of changes affecting their lists when they become known.

Breaking new ground

909. Experience has shown that when it is desired to bring the work of the Society and the advantages of life-saving training to the notice of a school or college, it can best be done initially by a letter addressed to the Headmaster or Principal supported by a copy of the latest Annual Report and the various pamphlets which can be obtained from the Headquarters on application. The letter should, if practicable, suggest a showing of the film "To Match Your Courage" with a supporting talk by a member of the Society. The Honorary Representative may on occasions feel that the first approach would come better from Headquarters in a letter sent on behalf of the National Executive, in which case the appropriate name and address and other relevant details should be sent to the Headquarters.

Expenses

910. Reasonable postage and travelling expenses incurred by Honorary Representatives will be refunded if claimed. Claims should be forwarded to Headquarters on 31st May and 30th November in each year, supported by brief details of each item for audit purposes. If an Honorary Representative accepts a request by Headquarters to conduct an examination outside his area involving additional expense, a separate claim for the refund should be made to

Headquarters as soon as possible after the examination has taken place.

911. Supplies of the Society's official notepaper, envelopes and examination forms are made to Honorary Representatives on request to Headquarters.

912. The National Executive welcomes brief reports by Honorary Representatives on the work in their areas, including suggestions for improvements, new ideas, notes on demonstrations given and so on. Such reports should reach Headquarters by 31st January so that reference to points of interest may be made in the Annual Report of the United Kingdom National Branch.

The Appointment and Duties of Examiners

913. Examiners carry out their duties voluntarily in support of the Society's work, and are appointed by the National Executive or by a Branch Executive Committee.

914. Each Branch Executive shall elect from amongst its Grade I Examiners, a special panel whom it considers to be competent in every way to conduct examinations of Candidate-Examiners. Two members of such a panel shall be required to conduct an examination. (In the case of non-branch areas and overseas areas, Headquarters will be responsible for devising a suitable arrangement.)

915. Applicants for appointment as an Examiner of the Society shall:

   (i) be over 21 years of age;

   (ii) hold at least the Bronze Medallion and have previous experience of the Society's work. Exceptional cases for appointment without these qualifications may be specially considered by the Branch or National Executive;

(iii) be recommended in writing by two Grade I Examiners;

(iv) be interviewed by a special interviewing panel or the Branch Executive as decided by the individual Branch, or in the case of a non-branch area, by a panel appointed by Headquarters, which may be the panel of an adjoining Branch.

(v) Submit themselves to an oral examination by the panel appointed;

(vi) undergo the Candidate-Examiner examination, except for the oral examination, which must be properly authorised by the appropriate authority before being held;

(vii) conduct an examination for the Bronze Medallion in the presence of two Grade I Examiners appointed for the purpose;

(viii) be subject to a probationary period for one year from the date of appointment.

916. If the applicant resides in a Branch area his application should be forwarded to the Honorary Secretary of the appropriate Branch; if outside the Branch areas, to the Secretary at the National Headquarters.

917. If the candidate-examiner passes his examination he will be appointed a Grade 2 Examiner and will be issued with an Examiner's Badge and a card of appointment authorising him to conduct examinations up to and including the Bronze Medallion and the Instructor's Certificates.

918. A Grade 2 Examiner may apply for appointment as a Grade I Examiner on the completion of the probationary period of one year provided that he has conducted examinations on six separate occasions.

If his application is accepted he will be required to conduct an examination for the Diploma, Distinction Award or Award of Merit in the presence of two specially appointed Grade I Examiners who will be responsible for examining both the Grade I candidate-examiner and the candidate(s) for the award. The candidate-examiner will be required to give his reasons for the marks which he has awarded the candidate(s) and to comment on the general performance of the candidate(s).

919. The National Executive reserves its own right and that of the Branch Executive Committees to refuse an application for appointment as a Grade 1 or Grade 2 Examiner without giving reasons for such refusal, and cannot engage in correspondence concerning such matters once a decision has been made. Similarly the right is reserved to remove an Examiner's name from the panel after giving due notice of such intention to the Examiner concerned at his last known address.

920. Each Branch and Headquarters may maintain a panel of Examiners authorised to conduct examinations for the Society's Safety Awards *only*. Such Examiners should satisfy the Branch Executive or Headquarters as to their competence and must be 18 years or over. _Safety Awards Examiners_

921. The Examiner will be solely responsible for the conduct of an examination but when a class of candidates is under examination the instructor of that class will be responsible for their safety. _Conduct of examinations_

922. On arrival at the place of examination the Examiner should satisfy himself that the examination forms have been correctly prepared, and should check the names (and ages in the case of a Bronze Medallion examination) of candidates present and that the number is not more than can be efficiently examined by the number of Examiners present and in the space available. The candidates should be paired so that each has a partner of approximately the same size and physique. The Examiner should check the measured distances for the tests, and the clothing of candidates (Bronze Cross and above) which may be old but must be clean and not modified in any way which would give assistance to the candidate.

923. It is not possible to legislate for every circumstance which may arise in the course of examinations for the Society's proficiency awards, and Examiners have authority to modify the rules and instructions contained in the *Handbook when necessary* provided that the test is not simplified and unfairness to the candidate does not result.

The relation of conditions in swimming baths to those in open water **924.** The purpose of the Society is to train people, very often young people, to save the lives of others from drowning. The success of the practical application of its teaching depends very largely on the Examiners who have the difficult task of not discouraging candidates for the Society's life saving proficiency awards and, at the same time, of ensuring that those awards are granted only to candidates who display the necessary high standard of performance. This balance between these two requirements, which to some extent conflict, has assumed added importance with the omission of age limits for awards other than the Bronze Medallion and the Diploma of the Society. Inevitably young candidates for the higher awards will be presented from time to time, and will perform all the required tests in a swimming bath despite the fact that their physique is such that if they attempted to put their knowledge to use in an emergency the result might well be the loss of their own life rather than the saving of another. The majority of examinations in the United Kingdom are of necessity conducted in swimming baths in which there is no wind, tide or current, and the water is warm. Any or all of these may be adverse factors in an actual rescue, calling for greater stamina and judgement on the part of the rescuer than is required in the examination. When informing candidates of the result of their examination Examiners should, on appropriate occasions, remind the candidates of these points and of the need for continued practice in life saving to ensure that if they are called upon to use their knowledge in an emergency, they will be able to achieve their purpose.

925. Reasonable expenses incurred by Examiners in the conduct of examinations on behalf of the Society will be refunded by the Headquarters or Branch if requested. Expenses

926. In order to keep the details recorded in the Examiners' Panels correct and up-to-date as regards addresses, changes of name, etc., Cards of Authority should be returned with a note of any changes to the Headquarters or the Branch, as appropriate, on the anniversary date in each year of the original date of issue. Return of cards of authority

927. Examiners who decide, or are forced by circumstances, to give up their appointment as an Examiner are requested to return their Cards of Authority and Examiner's badge to the Headquarters or the Branch, as appropriate, so that their names may be removed from the panel and difficulties, which otherwise arise in the arrangement of examinations, may be avoided.

928. Examiners are earnestly requested to inform the Headquarters or the Branch, as appropriate, of changes in their address. If possible notification should be sent before the change takes place and should give the date on which it becomes effective. Change of address

THE BRANCHES OF
THE ROYAL LIFE SAVING SOCIETY

931. As it is possible to make corrections to the list only when the *Handbook* is reprinted, the names and addresses of Branch Honorary Secretaries are not included in the following list of Branches. The names and addresses are printed each year in the Annual Report, and may be had at any time on application to the Headquarters. The Branches are:

Royal Life Saving Society—United Kingdom

Birmingham and District
Bristol and District
County of Sussex
Devon
Essex
Hertfordshire
Huntingdon and Peterborough
Kent
Leeds and District
Leinster, Munster and Connacht
Liverpool and District
Manchester and District
Middlesex
North Yorkshire
North Lancashire
Northumberland and Durham
Scottish
Sheffield and District
South Wales
Surrey
Ulster
Wessex (Dorset, Hampshire and Wiltshire)

Overseas Branches represented on the Commonwealth Council by the United Kingdom members

Gibraltar	Matabeleland
Hong Kong	Rhodesia
Malta	Zambia

Royal Life Saving Society—Canada

Alberta	Ontario
British Columbia	Prince Edward Island
Manitoba	Province of Quebec
Nova Scotia	Saskatchewan

Royal Life Saving Society—Australia

New South Wales	Tasmania
Northern Territories	Victoria
Queensland	Western Australia
South Australia	Fiji

Royal Life Saving Society—New Zealand

Auckland	Northland
Canterbury	Otago
Gisborne	South Auckland
Hawke's Bay	Southland
Manawatu	Taranaki
Marlborough	Wanganui
Nelson	Wellington

National Branches represented on the Commonwealth Council by the U.K. members.

Royal Life Saving Society—Trinidad and Tobago

Royal Life Saving Society—Jamaica

HONORARY REPRESENTATIVES

932. The names and addresses of the Honorary Representatives of the Royal Life Saving Society—

United Kingdom are published in the Annual Report, and can be obtained on application to the Head-quarters.

THE OFFICIAL BADGES

 933. The registered badge of the Society may be worn by holders of the Intermediate Certificate and higher proficiency awards. The badge with the Royal Crown superimposed may be worn as a LAPEL badge by Officers of the Society (including appointed Examiners and Honorary Representatives) and as blazer and costume badges by holders of the Diploma and Distinction awards. The badge with the Royal Crown superimposed MAY NOT otherwise be worn on uniform or other personal clothing.

Special costume badges without the Society's registered badge are available to holders of the Elementary and Unigrip Certificates.

The appropriate badges are manufactured in enamel as lapel badges and woven in silk on cloth for attachment to swimming costumes. The badges indicated below can be purchased by holders of the appropriate awards.

Note.—**When ordering badges, the following particulars must be given, and remittances should accompany order:**

    (1) Name of class.   (2) Awards held.
    (3) Year in which these were obtained.

BADGES WHICH MAY BE WORN BY HOLDERS OF THE INTERMEDIATE CERTIFICATE

Each

Ordinary enamel, size of 6*d.*, for coat (pin or
    stud) –   –   –   –   –   –   – 4*s.* 0*d.*

Silk for costume – – – – –	4s. 0d.
Boy Scouts (uniform), woven in silk – –	1s. 0d.
Girl Guides (uniform), woven in silk – –	1s. 0d.

SPECIAL BADGES

Bronze Medallion, enamel for coat, or silk for costume – – – – –	4s. 6d.
Bronze Medallion, enamel uniform badge (shank) – – – – –	5s. 6d.
Bronze Medallion (school uniform), silk –	1s. 0d.
Bronze Cross, enamel for coat or silk for costume – – – – – –	4s. 6d.
R.L.S.S. Instructor, enamel for coat or silk for costume – – – – –	4s. 6d.
Award of Merit, enamel for coat or silk for costume – – – – – –	4s. 6d.
Distinction Award, enamel for coat or silk for costume – – – – –	4s. 6d.
Diploma, embroidered silk for costume –	12s. 6d.
Diploma, enamel for coat – – –	6s. 6d.

Badges available to qualified members of the Life Guard Corps

Life Guard Corps, enamel for coat (pin or stud) – – – – – –	4s. 0d.
Life Guard Corps, in silk for costume – –	4s. 0d.
Life Guard Cadet Corps, in silk for costume	4s. 0d.

Other Badges

Elementary Certificate, costume badge –	1s. 6d.
Unigrip Certificate, costume badge – –	1s. 6d.
Advanced Artificial Respiration Award, costume badge – – – – –	1s. 6d.
Preliminary Artificial Respiration Award, costume badge – – – – –	1s. 6d.
Advanced Safety Award, costume badge –	3s. 0d.
Preliminary Safety Award, costume badge –	3s. 0d.

THE ROYAL LIFE SAVING SOCIETY
MOUNTBATTEN MEDAL

934. The Mountbatten Medal is awarded annually by Admiral of the Fleet The Earl Mountbatten of Burma, Grand President of the Society, to the holder of one of the Society's proficiency awards who performs the rescue adjudged the best of the year. The first such medal was awarded in 1951. The names of recipients of the Mountbatten Medal are inscribed on a panel in the entrance hall of the Society's Headquarters.

935. Members of the Society and others who hear of rescues of sufficient merit are earnestly requested to report the details to the Society. A form for reporting rescues for consideration in the award of the Mountbatten Medal may be obtained on application to the Headquarters. Completed reports of rescues made in the United Kingdom and Eire must reach the Headquarters within two months, and others within four months of the date of the rescue. Notwithstanding the foregoing rule, reports of rescues made in the last weeks of the year must reach the Headquarters by 15th February in the following year.

936. The Royal Life Saving Society is a teaching and examining body and *does not* grant rewards, other than the Mountbatten Medal, for saving life from drowning.

THE ROYAL HUMANE SOCIETY grants such rewards, and application for recognition should be made to

The Secretary,
WATERGATE HOUSE, YORK BUILDINGS, ADELPHI, LONDON, W.C.2.

THE COMPETITION TROPHIES

937. The rules for the trophy competitions can be obtained on application to the Headquarters or Branches.

938. The following four trophies are for competition throughout the Commonwealth Society.

THE KING EDWARD VII CUP, presented by His Majesty King Edward VII in 1902. The cup is awarded to the affiliated organisations showing the best results in life saving during the year.

THE GENERAL EXCELLENCE CUP, presented by Mr. W. F. Darnell in 1910. Competition is confined to Naval and Mercantile Training Ships, and to Naval, Military and Air Force service schools, colleges and training establishments.

THE WILLIAM HENRY MEMORIAL CUP, presented by the Rt. Hon. Lord Desborough, in 1928 as a perpetual memorial to the founder of the Society. The cup is awarded to the Branch of the Society achieving the best results in life saving during the year.

THE SYDNEY J. MONKS MEMORIAL TROPHY, presented by Mrs. R. A. Monks in 1936 as a memorial to her husband who was Chief Secretary of the Society. The trophy is for competition amongst the Branches of the Society.

939. The following trophies are for competition in the Royal Life Saving Society—United Kingdom:

JOHN V. HUDSON MEMORIAL TROPHY. A silver cup, presented by the Central Executive, London, in memory of John V. Hudson, Honorary Treasurer of the Society for twenty-one years. Open to all affiliated organisations (except Police Training Centres and Metropolitan Police Training Division).

THE DARNELL EXCELLENCE CUP, presented in 1910 by Mr. W. F. Darnell, is open to all Boys' Schools and Boys' Sections of Mixed Schools affiliated to the Society.

THE MRS. HENRY CUP, presented by Mrs. Henry in 1929, in memory of her husband (the founder of the Society). Open to all Girls' Schools and Girls' Sections of Mixed Schools affiliated to the Society.

THE AFFILIATED CLUBS' SILVER AND BRONZE CHALLENGE SHIELD, presented by the Bath Club in 1923. Open to all Ladies', Mens' or Mixed Swimming clubs affiliated to the Society.

SCHOOLS SAFETY AWARD CUP (formerly THE LADIES' SILVER-GILT CUP, presented in 1903 by the Putney Ladies' S.C.). Open to all Schools giving full-time education affiliated to the Society.

THE STUDENTS' SHIELD. Open to Colleges of Further Education affiliated to the Society.

THE SALVESEN SHIP (THEODORE SALVESEN MEMORIAL TROPHY), presented in 1966 by the Theodore Salvesen Memorial Trust. Open to Pre-sea students of Nautical Colleges or Nautical Departments of Established Colleges.

THE COLONEL WOODCOCK POLICE CUP, presented in 1930 by Col. H. C. Woodcock, D.L., J.P. Open to County and Borough Police Forces of Great Britain and Northern Ireland (Police Forces of Greater London excepted).

THE BEATRICE STAYNES LIFE GUARD CORPS TROPHY. A trophy in silver and enamel, a bequest to the Society by Miss Beatrice Staynes, formerly Honorary Representative for Leicester. Open to Life Guard Clubs and other Life Guard Corps organisations affiliated to the Society having not less than ten active senior (not cadet) Life Guard Corps Members.

THE PRIMARY AND SECONDARY MODERN SCHOOLS' NATIONAL SHIELD, presented in 1892 by Messrs. Lever Brothers Ltd., is open to all Schools giving full-time education, affiliated to the Society.

THE POLICE BATON, a trophy consisting of a silver-gilt Police Baton mounted upon an ebony plinth for competition between teams from Police Forces of the United Kingdom.

THE ALINGTON CUP, presented in memory of his daughter, Lady Alington, by The Right Hon. The Earl of Shaftesbury, P.C., K.P., G.C.V.O., C.B.E., LL.D., for competition between teams from Women Police Forces of the United Kingdom.

THE WEST RIDING CUP, presented by the West Riding Constabulary for competition between teams of Police Cadets.

LANDMARKS IN THE
GROWTH AND DEVELOPMENT
OF THE SOCIETY

1891—Inaugural Meeting on January 3, called by H. Hewitt
Griffin, F. W. Moses, E. W. Stafford, W. Brickett,
C. Val Hunter, A. Sinclair and W. Henry (first
Chief Secretary). First edition of the *Handbook*
published.

1893—His Royal Highness the Duke of York consented to
become President.

1894—First English (Manchester) and first Australian (New
South Wales) Branches formed.

1896—Diploma of the Society instituted.

1897—Formation of the Scottish Branch.

1898—Visit of the Life Saving Society to Sweden.

1899—Life Saving instruction adopted by the London
School Board.

1901—His Majesty King Edward VII consented to become
Patron of the Society. Tour in Italy by a team of
the Life Saving Society.

1902—The "King's Cup" presented by King Edward VII.
Tour in Germany and Austria by a team of the
Life Saving Society.

1904—The Society granted permission to use the title
"Royal." Formation of the Sheffield Branch.

1907—The Schafer Method of Resuscitation adopted.

1908—Award of Merit of the Society instituted. Formation
of the Ulster Branch.

1909—William Henry's tour of Canada. First Canadian
Branch formed (Ontario), first New Zealand
Branch formed (Wanganui).

1910—His Majesty King George V consented to become Patron of the Society.

The Lord Desborough, K.G., G.C.V.O., became President (Acting President since 1901).

William Henry's tour of Australia and New Zealand.

1913—Tour of South Africa by William Henry. South African and Southern Rhodesian Branches formed.

1924—A Royal Charter of Incorporation granted by His Majesty King George V. Malta Branch formed.

1928—Sydney J. Monks appointed Chief Secretary.

1929—Formation of the Bristol Branch.

1930—First Conference of the Home Branches held in London. Formation of the Liverpool and N. & D. Branches.

1931—The Society's instructional film "Saving Life from Drowning," produced and exhibited. Formation of the Leeds Branch.

1932—Publication of 19th edition of the *Handbook* completely revised. Formation of South Wales and N. & E. Yorks. Branches.

Life Guard Corps inaugurated.

1933—Bar to Bronze Medallion Examination instituted. Empire Conference held in London.

Tour of South Africa by Mr. J. C. Fishenden (Vice-President). Formation of the Birmingham Branch.

1934-5—Tour of Australia and New Zealand by Mr. H. H. Lock, Chairman of the Central Executive.

1935—Resuscitation Certificate Examination instituted.

Bar to Award of Merit Examination instituted. Formation of the L.M. & C. Branch.

1936—Capt. A. E. Biscoe appointed Chief Secretary.

Tour of Canada by Mr. J. C. Fishenden (Vice-President).

"Sea Water Diploma" Examination instituted.

1937—Publication of the 20th edition of the *Handbook*.

His Majesty King George VI consented to become Patron of the Society.

1938—The Society's examination figures reached a record of 105,710 successful candidates.

Her Royal Highness the Princess Elizabeth passed the Royal Life Saving Society's examination for the Intermediate Certificate.

1939—Her Royal Highness the Princess Margaret passed the Royal Life Saving Society's examination for the Elementary Certificate.

Outbreak of the Second World War. The booklet *Artificial Respiration — Are You Prepared?* issued. The work of instructing Civil Defence and National Fire Service workers in the art of applying Artificial Respiration undertaken. Minister of Home Security recognised the Society's special badge and permitted it to be worn on Civil Defence Uniform.

1942—Classes formed in prisoner-of-war camps, Germany.

1944—Her Royal Highness the Princess Elizabeth consented to become Vice Patron of the Society. Formation of the N. Lancashire Branch.

1945—The Society acquired new permanent Headquarters. Admiral The Lord Louis Mountbatten, G.C.V.O., K.C.B., D.S.O., A.D.C., consented to become President of the Society.

1946—Twenty-first revised edition of the *Handbook* published.

1948—The Chief Secretary created a Member of the King's most Excellent Order of the British Empire (M.B.E.).

1951—Her Royal Highness the Princess Elizabeth, Duchess of Edinburgh, attended the Diamond Jubilee Council Meeting and unveiled the Mountbatten Life Savers' Panel.

1952—Distinction Award Examination instituted.
Her Majesty Queen Elizabeth II consented to become Patron of the Society. Adoption of the Holger Nielsen Method of Artificial Respiration.
First demonstration of life saving on television arranged by Mr. Poulton.

1953—Conference of Home Branch Secretaries held in London.

1954—Visit of Mr. E. A. Pleydell, Honorary Secretary of the Australian Federal Council, to Headquarters.

1955—Captain Biscoe retired and Captain E. Hale, Royal Navy (Rtd.) became Chief Secretary. The Home Branches invited to accept membership of the Central Executive. Outline proposal for the re-organisation of the Society approved by the Council. Second Conference of the Home Branches held in London. Publication of 22nd revised edition of the *Handbook*.

1956—The President, accompanied by the Chief Secretary, visited Australia and New Zealand and attended meetings of the Councils, at which the reorganisation of the Society was discussed. The Australian Life Saving Society integrated with the New South Wales Branch of the Royal Life Saving Society. Conference of Home Branch Secretaries to discuss the draft Constitution for the U.K. National Branch. Medal awards and certificates reduced in size as an alternative to higher examination fees. Promotion of circulation dropped from artificial respiration drill.

1957—The annual total of awards exceeded 150,000 for the first time (157,886) Annual Council Meeting attended by the High Commissioners for Canada, Australia, New Zealand and South Africa. Admiral of the Fleet the Earl Mountbatten of Burma resigned as President and accepted office as the first Grand President of the Society. Proposals for the reorganisation of the Society approved by the Council. Formation of the Shadow Commonwealth Council. Appointment of the Administrative Committee. Appointment of Mr. A. C. E. Musk as Honorary Treasurer of the Society. Publication of the 16th edition of the *Artificial Respiration Handbook* and of the Australian *Modern Manual of Water Safety and Life Saving*. Formation of the County of Sussex, Essex, Middlesex, Isle of Wight and Surrey Branches.

1958—The Governments of the United Kingdom, Canada, Australia, New Zealand and South Africa asked to make financial grants to the Commonwealth Council. Appointment of the Medical Committee (Sir Cecil Wakeley, Dr. D. W. Brooks, Mr. W. P. Cleland and Professor Ronald Woolmer). The Chief Secretary attended a meeting of the South African Council to obtain final approval of the draft Supplemental Charter and visited the Branches of the Society in South Africa and Southern Rhodesia and Honorary Representatives in Kenya. He also attended a meeting in Saltzburg with representatives of life saving organisations of Austria, France, Holland, Western Germany, Italy and Eastern Germany to consider the formation of an International Life Saving Technical Committee.

1959—The Council invited the Medical Committee to make recommendations concerning the adoption of the Mouth-to-Mouth method of artificial respiration. The Chief Secretary attended meetings of the Councils in Canada, Australia and New Zealand to obtain final approval of the draft Supplemental Charter and visited the Australian Branches, the Ontario and Province of Quebec Branches. A resolution approving the submission of a petition for the grant of a Supplemental Charter to Her Majesty the Queen passed at an Extraordinary Meeting of the Council. Presentation of the Grand President's bell to commemorate the reorganisation of the Society. Introduction of the blue enamel Junior A.R. Badge. Visit of Mr. J. E. McCutcheon, Honorary Executive Secretary of the Canadian Council to the Headquarters. The Chief Secretary attended a Centenary Conference in the Hague arranged by the Orange Cross Society of Holland.

1960—27th January—Grant of the Supplemental Charter bringing into effect the new organisation of the Society. Appointment of His Excellency Rt. Hon. Sir Eric Harrison, K.C.V.O., High Commissioner for Australia, as Deputy Grand President of the Society. Sir Cecil Wakeley, Bart, K.B.E., C.B., F.R.C.S. elected the first President of the Royal Life Saving Society—United Kingdom, Sir Henry Studdy, C.B.E., Deputy President and Mr. A. C. E. Musk as Honorary Treasurer. Appointment of Captain L. de W. Lyons-Montgomery, Royal Marines, as Deputy Secretary of the Society. South Rhodesia and Matabeleland Branches transferred from the South African Council to the United Kingdom Council. The Grand President, during official tours, had discussions with the Canadian, Australian and New Zealand Presidents in Ottawa, Canberra and Wellington, and met members of the Society in Bulawayo, Nairobi, Mombasa, Aden, Kuala Lumpur, Singapore, Hong Kong and Fiji. The United Kingdom Council approved the Constitution for the United Kingdom National Branch for submission to Her Majesty's Privy Council. The Council invited the United Kingdom Medical Committee to make recommendations concerning the inclusion of external cardiac massage in the Society's teaching.

The annual total of awards issued by the Society exceeded 200,000 for the first time. Formation of the Huntingdonshire, Kent, Wessex and Mombasa Branches. The Canadian Council took over the issue and recording of awards in Canada.

1961—The first Commonwealth Conference of the Society was opened in St. James's Palace on 17th July by Her Majesty Queen Elizabeth The Queen Mother who accepted a brooch in the form of the Society's badge in gold and enamel as a memento of the occasion. Subsequently the delegates and other representative members of the Society were entertained by the Queen and Prince Philip at a sherry party in Buckingham Palace at which Her Majesty accepted from the Grand President the Patron's badge of the Society in gold and enamel.
The Expired Air method of artificial respiration adopted by the United Kingdom National Branch. The South African Council and Branches of the Society became the South African Life Saving Society following the declaration of South Africa a Republic outside the Commonwealth. The total number of life saving proficiency awards issued by the Society exceeded 4 million. Formation of the Devonshire, Hong Kong and Trinidad and Tobago Branches.

1962—H.R.H. The Prince of Wales gained the Elementary Certificate and the Bronze Medallion. H.R.H. Prince Richard of Gloucester gained the Bronze Medallion. Appointment of the Chief Secretary as a Commander of the Order of the British Empire. Lieutenant-General Guy Simonds, C.B., C.B.E., D.S.O., C.D., became President of the Royal Life Saving Society—Canada. Reorganisation of the Society in Canada. During the course of an official tour the Grand President met members of the Society in Jamaica to discuss the formation of a

168

Jamaica Branch, and accepted from the President and members of the Trinidad and Tobago Branch on behalf of the Commonwealth Council a Gavel to commemorate the formation of the Branch. Formation of the Hertfordshire, Aden, Gibraltar and Jamaica Branches.

1963—Publication of the first edition of the United Kingdom *Handbook of Instruction*.

The Jamaica and Trinidad & Tobago Branches became the Royal Life Saving Societies— Jamaica and Trinidad & Tobago.

1964—The Isle of Wight and Aden Branches dissolved voluntarily by the Branch Committees due to lack of adequate public swimming facilities.

H.M. The Queen approved the use of the Royal Crown with the badge used by the Royal Life Saving Society—United Kingdom.

1965—Captain Hale retired and Brigadier P. de C. Jones, O.B.E., became Chief Secretary.

1965—Sir Henry Studdy, C.B.E., succeeded Sir Cecil Wakeley, Bart, K.B.E., C.B., LL.D., D.S.C., F.R.C.S., as President of the United Kingdom Branch.

1966—75th Anniversary of the Society. Second Commonwealth Conference was opened on 18th July at St. James's Palace by H.R.H. Princess Margaret, Countess of Snowdon.

The delegates and other representatives of the Society were entertained at Buckingham Palace by The Queen and Prince Philip.

Formation of Zambia Branch.

Captain Lyons-Montgomery resigned from appointment of Deputy Secretary of the Society.

Mr S. R. Drinkwater, Chairman of the National Executive, appointed an Officer of the Order of the British Empire.

INDEX

*Printed in Great Britain by Spottiswoode, Ballantyne & Co. Ltd.,
London and Colchester*